CHILDREN OF THE BREATH:

A Dialogue in the Desert

by

Martin Chervin

CHILDREN OF THE BREATH
A Dialogue in the Desert
by Martin Chervin

ISBN # 1-891280-02-3

Library of Congress Catalog Card Number # 98-074519

© 1998 by CMJ Associates, Inc. Marian Publisher

CMJ Associates, Inc. Marian Publisher
P.O. Box 661 Oak Lawn, Illinois

Manufactured in the United States of America

CMJ ASSOCIATES
Marian Publisher
P.O. Box 661
Oak Lawn, Illinois 60454
www.cmjbooks.com

PREFACE

Friends of Martin Chervin's *magnum opus,* a version of which is before you, have often felt more than a little like the young Christopher Tolkien. Watching his aging father, British fantasy writer, J. R. R. Tolkien, draft yet another subplot to the sprawling epic *The Silmarillion,* the junior Tolkien had the sinking feeling that: a) his inventive parent was having far too much fun going off in new directions; b) the likelihood of the elder writer's finishing, polishing and shaping this lifetime's worth of material was growing more remote by the day; and c) that mammoth, daunting task had already been, however unconsciously, bequeathed to him.

Tolkien, of course, was right on all counts.

When Martin Chervin died of heart failure in 1993, the work-in-progress, which he called *Chiaroscuro,* lay about his work room and on computer disks, in dozens of drafts, some as fresh as the day of his death, some dating back more than twenty years. Large sequential sections of the novel were virtually complete; other, more recent additions, were in various stages of completion. In between were older, finished pieces which the author had yet to smooth into the whole structure.

The task of putting this small library into publishable form fell, fortunately, into the very best of hands — those of Chervin's daughters, Carla and Diana, who had, quite literally, grown up listening to their father's nightly readings of a work which was always in progress. (I remember seeing childhood crayon drawings of the Chervin's three children, Charles, Carla and Diana, on the family's refrigerator door, featuring scenes from their father's tale.) Like Christopher Tolkien — and with similarly happy results — the editors took the approach of separating out from this multilayered mass — with its parable and variations, modern overlays, and character digressions — the narrative core, the seed out of which the whole work originally grew: in this case, an epic meditation on the New Testament scene of the confrontation between Christ and Satan in the wilderness.

This is how Matthew's Gospel records the event:

"Then Jesus was led up by the Sprit into the wilderness to be tempted by the devil. And he fasted forty days and forty nights, and afterward he was hungry. And the tempter came and said to him . . ." (Mt. 4:1-3).

This is the messianic "testing" in the desert that, according to the synoptic Gospels, heralded the years of Jesus's active ministry, and, more importantly, his final meeting with his "adversary" on the cross. While the Gospel accounts highlight the three temptations to which Jesus was subjected by Satan during his desert ordeal, Chervin's work poses the sort of child's question that lay at the root of all good literature: "What did the two of them, Christ and Satan, *talk* about for forty days?"

Children of the Breath: A Dialogue in the Desert is an attempt to describe the vast contours of history's single greatest, and most consequential, conversation.

Of course, someone familiar with the whole work, as I was privileged to be, regrets the absence of one or another of the work's complex "layers," particularly Chervin's wickedly insightful Parable of the Wolf and the Lamb, with its twenty-one variations. But the editorial choices for this "performing version" of the novel are as sound as they are unsentimental. There is fine material that, one hopes, can find its way into print some day; but what the reader has in front of him is the essence of a book that traces not only the dramatic battle between Christ and Satan over the meaning of human history, but a vivid account of the lifelong preoccupations of a remarkable writer as well.

Abraham Martin Chervin was born into a poor Orthodox Jewish family on New York's lower Eastside on November 12, 1918. As a boy, he hawked wares on the streets and pressed flowers in a factory. Eager to explore life beyond the confines of an immigrant ghetto, Chervin haunted the New York Public Library, methodically emptying the shelves in alphabetical order. When he got to the New Testament — the ultimate 'forbidden' book for a boy from an Orthodox home — he expected the worst, but, instead, discovered Christ.

"Long before I believed anything," he once said, "I loved Him." Perhaps even more characteristically, he once granted that the New Testament might be divinely inspired because the words of Jesus were the only thing he'd come across that he couldn't edit.

After a stint in the service, he went into the first of a dozen entre-preneurial business enterprises he pioneered over the years. From owner of a coffee house in Greenwich Village in the heyday of the New York poets and the Beats, to sales representative for the Nelson and Sons' Revised Standard Version of the bible, to importer of art books, to editor of an employment journal for minorities, Martin was the inspiration for businesses he yielded to others, the develop-er of others' winning sales strategies, the agent of brilliant cam-paigns of which he soon tired.

In the late Fifties, Martin courted the young philosophy student and fervent Catholic convert, Ronda de Sola, also from a Jewish background, and in 1962, they were married in Rome. For nearly 15 years, until Martin's baptism in 1978, he admired, resisted, fought, dismissed, debated with and adored his wife's all-consuming commitment to Christ and the Church.

It was during these years — the years of his marriage to Ronda, the richest of Martin's life — that he began to force his struggles into words.

It came tumbling out of a box one evening in the early 1970's onto the dining room table in the Chervin house in Los Angeles: the plot that Martin had sketched for a great work of fiction, notes he'd compiled since his days as a seaman, a big, bold, sprawling work, worthy of a lifetime, on the Temptations of Christ. What I heard, then, on that evening, was a jumble of ideas. Before long, however, it was a great deal more than that, as Martin, year by year, settled down into the disciplines of a writer's life.

Not that the author of **Children of the Breath** was particularly prolific. A fine one-woman play, *Myself, Alma Mahler,* on the rela-tionship between Alma Schindler and the Jewish-Christian sym-phonist Gustav Mahler — not surprisingly, Martin's favorite com-poser — played counterpoint with the Christ and Satan novel dur-ing the 1970's. Premiered in New York and championed in more recent years by actress Pamela Fields, the play puts genius in the "dock," with Alma Mahler in the role of prosecuting attorney. Multi-dimensional, as all Chervin's best work is, it appears as a kind of theatrical echo to the Christ-Satan saga. Here the terrible mystery of art ultimately confounds, and silences, the savvy objections of "talent," as the silence of Christ ultimately confounds, but fails to cancel, the devil's brilliant observations on the even more mysterious reality of holiness.

The anti-abortion play *Born/Unborn* occupied Chervin, along with his perennial re-workings of the *magnum opus*, during the 1980's. Literarily outclassed by his other works, even this "tendentious" drama set in an abortion clinic, has Chervin's characteristic virtue: his "villains," however misguided, are never allowed to be anything less than sympathetic, and they are always given the best lines.

Readers of *Children of the Breath* will doubtless be reminded of other writers who tackled the great scriptural themes. The formidable Satan of Milton's *Paradise Lost* and the silent, loving Christ of Dostoevsky's *The Grand Inquisitor* come easily to mind.

But if there are literary antecedents for the bold, unflinching questions this novel poses, they are not the Western classics, but, rather, the unsparing and wide-ranging homiletic inquiries of the tradition of Jewish *midrash*. A scholar once called the midrashic mind "the wild West of the intellect." The midrashic writers of the early Christian centuries delved into the Scriptural narratives in search, not of moral or philosophical principles, but of the rich and complex human dramas they contain. Full of faith, they never allowed their convictions to place boundaries on the scope of their questions. Not content with easy answers, midrash explores the dark corners of the Bible, the dilemmas it poses, but does not solve — short, that is, of the luminous silence of God.

W. H. Auden once posited that people become writers because they're trying to address an intractable dilemma in their lives. Martin ultimately "solved" the "problem" that informs the pages of his novel: he came to believe in the Christ he had always loved. Thankfully, however, like his Jewish forebearers who wrote the Scriptures, he had the good sense not to hide the wounds, or evade the wisdom inflicted by the struggle.

There's a reason that Martin could not finish this book: It was, in effect, the vehicle through which he recorded seventy years of wrestling with the One he called "The radiant figure of Christ" — an enterprise on which he was engaged to the very end.

— Gabriel Meyer

CONTENTS

CHAPTER ONE
CREATION MINUS ONE

"Who would have dared to challenge Creation
if, at the close of each new day,
God said 'It is perfect.'
Instead, His lips spoke 'It is good. . .'
and the serpent
was already in Eden."

—*Satan*

Part 1
REHEARSAL

It was raining in the desert.

There was no wind, so the descent was unwavering, sheeting in panels of ice-pointed missiles. Strange for the desert!

Jesus had just arrived.

The sand lost the imprint of moisture quickly enough: deep, dry, centuries-old reservoirs, accepting all that was given. Nevertheless, the rain continued, unabated in intensity, even penetrating the heated undersurface where glowing pellets of silica seethed in the burning furnace.

Suddenly, what had seemed interminable subsided in an instant. Now, the sun was blazing through the higher mists, its rays beckoning all moisture backward like crooked fingers.

From every pore on the surface of the sand, clouds of steam erupted. Miniature volcanoes pockmarked the length of the desert, jetting spouts of vapor, befogging the lower surface with thick banks of swirling clouds.

Jesus, submerged, did not panic, knowing that his summons to the desert was in the name of Life. He waved his hands before his eyes, trying to penetrate the haze. "Your labor is it, Satan?"

The reply came in tiny-throated bits of laughter like shattered glass, breaking off self-consciously.

Jesus spoke calmly. "Of *such* is the signature of your spirit? Must Satan hide and crouch like a beast before his entrance?"

A flutter of wings overhead. Startled, Jesus raised his head and saw two birds perched on an invisible bough, a crow and an owl. Each one took turns fanning off the mist while the other spoke. There was neither art nor design in this display of puppetry, nor was much of an attempt made to conceal the common throat of the prompter, further serving the mockery.

The owl turned to the crow, "Is this my own, my beloved son?"

The crow nodded vigorously, "Yes, Father. But you sent a dove! Why didn't you send a crow? Even an owl! Better still, couldn't YOU come—just because dove rhymes with love, ugh!"

The owl shook its head until feathers dropped off its wings, adding to its bedraggled and loosely-stuffed appearance. "Me?! Down there?! Hoot!"

"But Father, thy will! Thy will! Guide me lest I fall among the sinful!"

"Hie thee then to the desert! Chew on your soul like a cud for a while ... let's say forty days, a good mystical number. There I will raise Satan to instruct thee, that you may know the ways of evil and become informed in matters more worldly than the ways of carpentry...."

"Satan!!!!"

The birds were jerked up and out of view.

Jesus was not easily provoked. The mist merged with a protruding belly of clouds and as he strained forward, he became aware of clusters of eyes, hanging like grapes on both sides of him, burning through the fog with their intensity. Their focus, he saw, was not himself but farther ahead where the thick bank of clouds was now rising like an opening curtain. There was the vaguest sound of voices in polyphony, chanting, "To what decease has life begun?"

A severed body lay on the ground, hands still reaching for a head that was not there. Inches away, only the back of the head had been visible: now, by some inexplicable momentum, the head rolled over.

Jesus gasped in horror then moaned in anguish ... this had been the face of John, by whose hands the living water had fallen, himself now baptized by his own gore. Jesus cried out in pain and at the sound, a rat leaped out of John's open, grief-stopped, prayer-ended mouth, scampering off on tiny, red-stained feet.

"Thus, truth from the mouth of the prophet!" This time, the voice of the hidden commentator rang, full and ripe. Without hesitation, Jesus replied, "Thou, who hast seen the wonder of creation, can you conceive this end?" Then, as the music entered his rhythm, he continued, "Naught that was there in the beginning that will not be there at the end, not the hair of a child, not the flash of a star ...

pull off the wings of the butterfly, yet it will fly to its day of Judgment!"

"The end!" The severed head and body was thrust into sharper relief against the fog. "Do you ask how? Why? The last Master changes the End, edits the Before. For now, raise your head above myth, take courage without dogma, look back to the very beginning, the first Before!"

"In the beginning was the Word, and the Word..."

"Nonsense, m'boy, nonsense! We're down deep now! There's no room in the pit for a poet's invention. In the beginning was silence: the un-creation. There was no Word, no shape, form, letter, or alphabet ...before. But where did it come from, that frozen instant of conception? Lo, errant thought!

"Call it what you will, Jesus ben Joseph. Nor did I come here to find an apostle! And if your imagination can't transcend words (the first Word!) at least hold onto my tail: I'll take you further. Behind the thought, there is the one who thinks. Before the one who thinks, there is the one created to think.

"That's why your brain is caged in, Jesus. So it can't escape and try to survive independently in a sea of floating slime. ...But looking further beyond the Word, before the long ago where Pater is one paternity within *Mater Perpetua*—ONENESS—without birth, without growth, unaged, yet already hoary, with wrinkles within wrinkles. He who creates and was not created!

"There you are, Jesus! Look to Him! The mysterious laborer! He, the one enfolded in shroud and swaddling clothes—the end and the beginning! Master of Creation! He, the primeval pulse from whom all origin takes origin! He, the shatterer of silence!

"Go on, Jesus, yes, go on. I know why you are here, why I must give ear to this troubadour while he beguiles me with melody and invention. Strum! Strum! What words do you strum in His name? Tell me, is it you, the Messiah?"

Meanwhile, the strangeness in the desert had expended itself, the last tiny wisps fluttered away. The spirit that was Satan was now plainly visible, having taken on the unobtrusive flesh of a middle-aged gentleman of substance. It was a non-pretentious, plasticized disguise that could not begin to contain the fire and fury that flared so often beyond its circumference.

Jesus looked at the twisted, smiling face before him and made no effort to restrain his repugnance. Even this debonair nonchalance was a form of mockery. The eyes were glittering now, forcing attention to themselves, now the head was bent forward, coming closer, and the voice piped out the stretched throat on the edge of laughter, "Come, Jewsus," it hissed, "I am thy burning bush!"

The power was unmistakable, and the vow of Forty Days took on substance, sounding a whisper on drums. Jesus tried to look back steadily into the browed eyes of his opponent, meeting the challenge, "In the beginning without beginning, pre-eminent, pre-existent, *ADONAI*. What was to be was caressed by grace, was blessed by presence, and that which was spirit, of itself sacred, was further sanctified of its own essence, soul of its soul."

Jesus' voice had grown tremulous, only too well aware that before him, cloaked in the ridiculous guise of a bourgeois gentleman, was no less than the Spirit of Rebellion. The eyes were on him with a sting, alert for any clue toward corruption. Jesus flared up first, "What thou wouldst undo, thou couldst not have done!" Then the sternness left his face as he returned to his theme. "Within the aura of that harmony—whose perfection is joy, whose joy is perfection—overflowing joy, irrepressibly free, perpetual, replenishing crystalline facets, spurting, leaping, pirouetting sprays, ecstatically in movement, dancing higher, *in ultimo*, Love."

In his impulsiveness, surprising even Satan, he had reached out to touch the hair-covered hand, pressing its fingers. "The source, Satan, the source!"

He looked gratefully upward, so that Satan, following his glance, almost expected to see God above them, watching benignly. By now almost intoxicated, Jesus continued, "Thus were the spheres set on notice, having gone beyond extravagance, the pulse and the throb and the flow entered eternity. Now..." Jesus stopped and breathed deeply, eyes closed, as if filling his lungs with the perfumes of day and the musk of night when first, and most purely, they were ordered so. "Now, the expectant silence ceases trembling, suddenly

... the light! Father to the first fires, pre-resurrectional! Where once was naught, now, a burst of warmth and holiness. This moment, YES, this moment, YES, when all tongues held love, burning YES, YES, love! *Then ...was spoken ...the Word!*'

Satan had learned to listen. If one is the image of Negation, devoted to the flaw and ever in pursuit of the imperfect and contradictory, one develops inner sensory perceptions and a talent for the intuitive that surpasses all obstacles. When Satan cocks an ear or narrows his glance, the prison of bone and flesh clangs open, exposing the naked spirit. His plan for Jesus had been most forthright: sound out the weak spots, intuit the flaw, see where the bribe will take, give as little as you can (or take back later), and go to it!

During the whole of Jesus' elegiac statement, Satan had every pore open, absorbing the letters of each word, sponging up inflections, examining the length of pauses, vaguenesses, ascents, descents; shifting the contents in glaring lights and reflective mirrors; probing the view from microscopic closeness and telescopic distance, smelling, sniffing, touching with his fingertip, biting the bones between his teeth, licking the vowels and chewing the consonants; measuring it in other times, other spaces, against what had been written or said before; repeating it over and over again to feel the effects of monotony and rote; hurling phrases to study their echoes, weighing the shift of emotion against subsidiary experience ... all this adding up to—NOTHING!

Most frustrating.

Now came a curious moment. Satan seemed to dissolve within himself, forming a compact mass of furious energy which fed on the guise he had most recently assumed, becoming the more comfortable bestial form: three faces and six wings. All three mouths worked together, spouting forth, "Gaze upon me and die, Jesus!"

Jesus, however, did not turn aside; nor did he show signs of alarm, recognizing the terrible need of Satan to drop all caution and expose himself. There followed a flashing series of transformations, serpent to a toad, a crow, a loathsome old hag, and finally, once more, the inoffensive, pot-bellied member of the bourgeoisie, all in the flicker of an eyelid. He bowed with affected graciousness, remarking casually, with a semi-apologetic air, "You must understand that I studied under the First and Foremost Illusionist."

Neither now nor at any time would Jesus be able to conceal his aversion to Satan's casual blasphemies. Satan, seeing how perfectly he scored the target, held inventory for future opportunities.

He came close to Jesus now, shaking out his sleeves like a magician before his act, and indeed, he produced in each hand a ball that had not been there before. He brought one ball close to Jesus for inspection. It was a horror! The stretched membranes were amnions, partially filled with life-supporting fluid to feed human embryos in fetation.

"Adam!" he held out one globe, "Eve!" and then the other. Tiny arms and legs were struggling for balance on the slippery membrane.

Satan chuckled, eyeing Jesus with great amusement, "They dream of life."

Satan stepped back a few paces and began juggling the globes, wryly commenting, "They would seek larger globes, dominion over beasts, the space they occupy, the entire earth!"

Jesus knew that Satan intended to drop the globes—there was no suspense in that—yet he raised a hand in protest, feeling the anguish of unfulfilled birth.

Satan pretended to fumble, clowning his missteps. "And after the earth, the oceans, the heavens, the sun, the moon, the stars ... even the giant ball that surrounds: Him!"

With one great heave and then another, he threw the amnion balls at the curtain of the sky, turning his back with complete indifference as to where or how they fell.

He turned his full attention to Jesus, watching him with deep concentration for some time. He saw without empathy, disregarding anything that might intrude on or dilute the precise and perfect tyranny of his own will.

"Are the liquids running out, Jesus? Are they merging ... arms and legs in embrace? Perhaps one final sigh, Jesus?"

It was Jesus who sighed. He spoke softly, "This will not be forgiven thee."

"Ends, Jesus, not beginnings!" Satan laughed contemptuously. "Forever reversed, first creation, then Judgment Day ... shouldn't judgment come first? Unless the flaw was the true intention? And the crime made for the pleasure of the judge? Beginnings, Jesus, not ends!" Satan reared at the memory of some terrible wound, then continued, "In the beginning was silence, minus an errant angel's lingering note ...minus an angel! Something before nothing, before something, without end or beginning, having dominion unto itself, to itself unchallenged, hovering over the void, pondering, brooding, rehearsing—seeding the drama.

"Then that first, greatest of shouts: I am! From that pregnant Breath, a cloud of angels burst forth, singing, contending for His praise with their Hosannas. Thus, the open-lipped gape begging sustenance. Thus, the ache of distant loneliness, unformed, but forming, confounded in the matrix with the ennui of power unused, abused. Thus, a snap and sudden reflex, the muscles of the Great Spirit tightening, while the eye invades the ungenesized."

Jesus heard him out, knowing the fault in his heart, cradling within his mind and consciousness what Satan had admitted. Yet, he hesitated before replying, wondering how it was possible that this wit and intelligence, once so near to God could disregard that most central core that comes so naturally to the newborn beast and nurtures the child of man.

Replying to Satan, he did not choose the sword. Instead, he brought forth the truth as it sang within his heart, letting it shimmer with its own light, trusting its own unique power to illuminate all the false and misleading shadows. He spoke to the sky, "In the beginning was Love, and Love was with God and God was Love. Before the birth, the Mystic-Lily, already born, was revealing itself between sprays of white petals until the orange heart burned through. It is music between silences, illuminating the signature, opening shell upon shell of darkness to reach the innermost pouch. Thus, the timid spirit, the about-to-be, is drawn through warmth and water into the loving light. What a radiant bloom! Petals! Perfume! After this, could there be less than forever and a day? Can all the powers of darkness prevail against it?

Satan was furious. Blowing out his breath and stamping his foot while Jesus spoke, he now took advantage of the first pause to intervene, pushing Jesus aside, raising his voice in a fit of temper. "Stand aside, little prophet, Jesus, Messiah, or whatever name suits your fancy. This tongue is not for your ears. I speak *ex cathedra*! When I pray, nobody watches!"

Satan backed away a good distance, looked upward, arms stiffly by his side, and addressed himself to God in a language that was neither Hebrew nor Aramaic.

"Lord, I call upon You with all the names You like to hear; Dispenser of Truth, Mediator of Justice, Light of the World. I call upon you in the name of God, in the name of Jehovah, in the name of Adonai. I whisper within myself that secret name unknown to other tongues, unshaped by another lip. Hear me!

"Unto this wilderness I came, answering thy summons: I came in my loneliness—my loneliness knowing thine—in kindred anguish.

"Yet I must take exception to Your way with me: Thou with pride for justice. If this is your Messiah, my Lord, with all due respect I must say that either the clay is wearing thin—or is it that the Potter has grown weary and disenchanted?

"Your way with me, Lord, is scarcely fitting even toward the least of your sons. Yet is Satan deposed less than Raphael or Gabriel? The black halo shines no less, my Lord.

"Forty days of this sniveling, groveling sycophancy can be more burdensome than the pack on the back of Adam. At first, I could hardly find him, buried to his neck in sand, mumbling prayers, and screaming (yes, screaming!) at his own shadow (as if I don't have enough of this in Sheol).

"If he were one of my own, gone demented, well and good. But his feverish eyes already contemplating some imaginary martyrdom ... who is he anyhow? What game are we playing now? Tell me, Lord. I know that mine are always the black pieces. You know that I start every game certain to win ... both of us recognizing the inherent weakness of Your side. The pawns fall. Here and there, a major piece. I stand poised; ready to swoop down and sweep up the board; 'Checkmate!' forms in my throat ... and You change the rules!

"You invent mercy, manipulate forgiveness, and, as if that were not enough—hoopla—in the name of *Love* I see your dead pawns being 'redeemed,' brought back to life on Your side of the board. And it doesn't end there! Lo and behold, I find myself standing by, lamely watching, as You convert my black pieces to white ones.

Really, Lord, forgive me for saying so … You know that I can't refuse to play … have I any hope of winning?"

Satan turned about without expecting or waiting for an answer. He looked at Jesus, discerning at once that Jesus had understood. His eyebrows came together and he smiled mischievously.

It was a young and eager man who came to this encounter; the strands of his hair still retaining the waters of baptism, his eyes aglow in the spirit of his mission. This selfsame irrepressible enthusiasm made the leap toward Satan a venturesome, if improbable, possibility—not devoid of hope.

"Thou, who hast seen the stars fall out of the sky; thou, who hast touched the cloak of the Divine; thou, spanning horizons where less worthy truths become false."

Satan stared incredulously at the disrespect, the impertinence, of this mere youth. Yet, he felt tolerant, even indulgent toward Jesus: such warmth, such a readiness to become soft with love. Satan filed away that inward vision under 'Flaw' for later probing.

Jesus continued, "Wanderer, look back the long and weary way: pride in the dust, the dead star exhausting its fire. What brings solace? The kind and cool stream, the balm, to burning feet, the door, wide-open … home! Where Love invites the uninvitable, giving a Welcome to Mercy: *thrice thy sins are forgiven!*"

"Mercy!" Satan exploded with astonishment. He had anticipated something like this, careful to consider all premises, priding himself on never being surprised. Yet, here he was, surprised by what he had already contemplated. This was too rarefied for belief....

"Are you offering me a bribe?" Satan looked upward with all the flavor of melodrama. "Did *You* hear that?"

As the silence settled, Satan came forward and bowed in circles as if he were acknowledging waves and bursts of applause. In a weird, almost comic, contradiction to the bourgeois pose he had adopted for the occasion with Jesus, Satan shuffled closer with the air of a buffoon sharing a great and personal secret with his audience.

"He ... llo, out there, hell ... o! Here I am, Satan ben Lucifer, lately of Sheol. There now! Don't draw back and gather up your skirts. I'm not really so terrible. If you should disagree with me, it's not so bad! I might even concede a little bit here, a little bit there ... we'll change the whole performance, if you don't like it. I have no prejudices that lean on truth: if you lean too hard, it falls over anyway, so get on with it, you pompous holy-of-holies who wouldn't change a phrase, a word, a comma, a period ... not even to save their souls.

"At least show yourself! Jesus, you call yourself? Fine, Jesus it will be. But here we are, only a day into the Forty and you've raised up such a cloud of litanies and wrapped yourself in so many layers of prayer that who can see you?!

"Be naked with me, Jesus. Come as you are. Leave behind such persuasions meant only to curry favor with Him. He doesn't need it! Nor were we brought head-to-head to un-influence one another. Just remember: after you're gone, I will still be!

"Make your commotion. Blow hard and call it a tempest. Build yourself a mountain of words ... Mercy, indeed! Kindness, why? Forgiveness, for what? Love, love, love, love, love. Let it all dribble out and away! I want to see you ... only you! I have no love for thee, nor thee for me. To the bone, Jesus! Off your knees and down to what defines us. Not forty days! I need only ten—a night or two!"

Part 2

SECOND MOVE:
BLACK PAWN TOWARD WHITE KING

First day of the Forty. The apprehension of those early hours was past, yet the incredible magnitude of what lay behind the approaching set of the sun was eased by the hungry yearning for prayer. God must be spoken to. Jesus turned his face from whence the sun had risen rather than where it was going.

Satan felt humiliated. It had not occurred to him that he might be dismissed so casually, even ignored, as Jesus bowed in the dust and began his prayers. He waited, but Jesus was swaying back and forth on his knees, looking upward with closed eyes, his lips moving intensely.

"Is your Heaven my Hell or my Heaven your Hell?" Satan howled.

"What hast thou wrought without faith?" began Jesus, but Satan never let him finish.

"Don't let me hear that word again! Take your Faith and put it beside Love and put that beside Good and Evil. Cast it all into Eternity! It's all been said before, deadly boredom—unspiced, unpalatable, untrue. We weren't brought together to exchange platitudes, to entertain phrases from each other with polite genuflections. Be naked, I say, let go! Eradicate the arbitrary, let's see what's underneath: the beginnings before beginnings, Jesus! In the beginning was ... SILENCE!"

Jesus took a step backward, away from the blast of hot breath. He replied sparingly, making an effort to be calm, recognizing the danger of allowing Satan to frame the environment. "What of those who see, and will not see? Has faith no eyes? What is it to see, and see clearly only one's own reflection? If it is possible to see at all with vain ambition and false pride."

Caught up in waves of increasing rage, it would seem that Satan must open the overflow in some outpouring of violence. Indeed, he turned purple and sputtered through compressed lips, beat on his sides with frustration while he dug his heels into the ground. Then, in an instant, he turned to Jesus with a pleasant smile as if he were merely replying to a simple question. "Really, Jesus ben Joseph, you do surprise me! How am I to intrepret your complete lack of curiosity? Here we are together, a good forty days and nights before us. Are you afraid of me? Even if it only concerned your own destiny (and you know that I've pored over the secret signs and symbols) wouldn't you permit yourself even one question? Yes or no?"

Suddenly, Satan became good-humored, eyeing Jesus up and down indulgently. "No, you don't want to know—or you don't believe I have the answer. Very well. Let's look elsewhere. You will concede, before you began, I was there! At the beginning before the beginning, Creation, I was there! Your perfect witness, rabbi! Question me, Jesus. I'm brimming over with answers! I'll open the sacred texts to you, for you alone, Jesus, the gospel before time, before the Word was burned into your flesh, the secret wars, the revolt, thou would-be Prince of the Earth ... see it as God saw it a day before Creation. I know it all, rabbi, and I'm honoring you. I dare you to look back and not become a pillar of salt! Come with me—you needn't hold my hand—why do you stand there, blinking at me so timidly! First, God spoke with Satan!"

Satan drew himself together, regarding Jesus speculatively. Although his listener had been fully attentive, it was obvious that he had not made true entry. He sliced the air with the palm of his hand. The air between them once more grew heavy with mist and Satan resorted to his opening gambit, becoming invisible while a chorus of catcalls and raw obscenities invaded the atmosphere. The moment was less than worthy, as even Satan must have recognized, for shortly afterwards he emerged, at least as a disembodied voice, piercing the thick fog. "Whose finger dared stir the endless seas? Who violated that single grain of infinity, breaking it off as one breaks bread, then tossing it with slack indifference into the precious void within darkness?"

Satan reappeared in a whirling cloud of dust atop a wild red horse. He lurched to a sudden halt just short of Jesus, backing off while his horse reared on its hind legs, front feet pawing the air.

Jesus could not help speculating on the elapsed time between Satan's sudden exits and entrances. That there existed arcane strands and bindings, cobweb filaments in a network of back and forth impulses between Satan and his forces was becoming only too real. Even now, in that instant just gone by, with a quick wrench, Satan had won the race with the repentance of someone's soul (the joy was in his face) and now there was a new dead star in the night.

Satan, reading his thoughts, looked down at him from the top of the horse, commenting broadly, "The breach is never too small." He leapt off his horse and strode up to Jesus, raising his foot as if to kick, then restraining himself, shouting instead in Jesus' ear, not to be ignored, "I came to you! When the Spirit tunneled into my realm, I came to you! I will not be less nor more when I leave because we were together."

Satan's storm subsided, giving way to strange chuckling sounds, his tribute to his own cleverness. "Now, to the point! Who tempts whom? If you have an offer to make to me, state your terms, give me your Source. And what guarantees? Do I get more than I give? What's the profit?"

Satan was becoming hilarious, jumping up and down, lending a farcical air to the act he was preparing. "And if all who dealt with me asked the same, how poor I'd be!" He danced around Jesus, making it difficult for him to concentrate. "On the other hand, have you some special desire?" he bent his face toward Jesus, with an all-knowing, worldly smile. His eyes twinkled cynically. "Have you an ambition, a little sophisticated whim, even a pretty fantasy fetched from afar...? A mission, perhaps? King of the Jews? Or would you sit with me and we'll gossip about Creation"what God won't tell you!" Satan drew himself into a tight ball, and hissed, "We'll whisper, like servants in the hall, we'll whisper so that the Master pays us no heed ... I saw it ... I saw it all ... through the keyhole."

Finally, Jesus had to respond. He rallied to the veer toward blasphemy, interrupting Satan with an outcry, "Look to yourself, Satan! How far have you fallen?"

Satan was wounded: underneath the surface of mockery, not even the moderating bourgeois pose Satan had adopted could entirely overlay the bilious bulge of purple veins in choleric pulsation under his smooth cheeks and about his throat. "You don't waste words do you? The virtue of caution. What you don't say can't be held against you, eh? How about numbers? Do you traffic in numbers? Forty, for example. Isn't that the number of days and nights in this wilderness? Didn't you know, weren't you warned ... forty is the number of catastrophes! It took just that many days to peak the Ark, conceding mistake with mistake. I seem to recall that Moses took the same number of days on a mountain talking to the sky, then returning, defined the ten best reasons for my prosperity. Then, forty years of manna wasted on a wilderness, like this one, just to keep a vain promise to Abram. Then, look at poor Elijah. He got nothing but sore feet on that forty-day and night trudge to Mount Horeb! But tell me, Jesus. Do you like numbers?"

Now was the fellness of the night. But for the restlessness of Satan, peace would have fallen and all would have been put aside for the next dawning. He paused in his pacings, observing Jesus at his prayers, heard him beseeching guidance, strengthening his faith, strengthening! How does one penetrate the hard shell of this one without crumbling the core? Satan understood that the prize must be intact or there would be no victory. Jesus' hands were upraised, fingers pleading.

Already, time was closing in beyond the day that was now gone by and the distance that remained. All the elements reformed themselves to make concession to what was about to transpire. It would seem that past, present, and future were out of sequence. Time, without a T, without an I, without an M, without an E.

The drums are circling the intake of breath to launch the COMMAND. Trumpets! Ready to be italicized! Now, it would be as it never was before but for that one uncounted event when there was no counting and no other eye was available, The Word forms on the tip of His tongue.

Hunger extrudes from the great Emptiness and there is yearning where His eye has not yet deigned to rest. Minus eight, minus seven, minus six, minus five, minus four, minus three, minus two, minus one. Out of the void, time spills into being, being enters existence, rising from spacelessness. It is morning.

CHAPTER TWO
CREATION ACCORDING TO SATAN

"Only a ripple moved over the unwrinkled face of all the sleeping waters. Great hollows yawned in their depths, surprised in the midst; always in the midst; the midst that acknowledges new beginnings, and interruptions, but never an ending ... in the midst of a dream.

The pulse was sameness.

And the ripple was slave to the COMMAND; gathering momentum, until sleep lost its eternity; shattering, splitting apart, and staring horrified at its open wound. The sharp edges of light sprang in with a shriek. The invasion! A blinding streak of light cutting through the black waters ... desperately pursued by green-threading waves vainly struggling to fill in the gap...

And what had been before and forever was never again to be."

–Satan

Part 1

CREATION +1

Thus, we arrive at the close of the first day ... the first day, the first sin: *the crime of the light.*

And the light saw its own nakedness, and was ashamed. Left to itself, it would have submerged quickly into the shelter and comfort of that ever-streaming bosom, *Master Generiis.* A slight burn. Scar, scarcely visible. But the light had been provided for; the indecency-become-flagrant was perpetuated by COMMAND. Separate! Henceforth, Day; henceforth, Night.

In the birth of time, a bastardy *sans amour,* Day and Night were chosen without choice to consummate a marriage without union; sharing their separate cosmos, above and below in turn, sharing defeat equally.

What is this force that changes 'beginnings' that never were into ends that can never be? Is there a whimsy other than Satan's, asking questions that answer themselves and are their own commentary?!

Think of the Night as in love with its owness; an unhorizoned, billowed and purple softness, slumbrous in its first cradle; rocking, drifting ... suddenly to have the burst, the clamour, the blaze of garish light fostered on it! To be compared, confined, conducted, compressed, contradicted ... besides, made smaller, ridiculed, forced to hammer its own links and imprisoned!

Thus, tampered with, and forced to clamp barnacles on the outer side of heaven to keep what remained intact; the Night hardened deep inside its billows, forming a last-stand barrier; becoming darker and more ominous; resisting, absorbing, suffocating whatever was foreign within, becoming a murderer's cloak, and a sickness unto the light.

Bring a new force into being (no matter how small the ripples!) the changed rhythms will never again be as before. Is God the same?

Suddenly, the Word! All those uncounted seconds, minutes and

years; those centuries, aeons and epochs; those formidable millenni-
ums, multimillenniums, and universal cycles … all stretched to the
outermost limits of memories forgotten to be remembered … He
remembers! Who else is eternal to His own eternity?

Was He careless? Could it be called indolence? Was it less pride
than playfulness … as simple as a cat's paw in a ball of twine? The
end product of boredom? In between a yawn and a snore? What
ended the benign will that had left all at rest and motionless?

Suddenly, the Word, the COMMAND! Why?

No matter! Peace, placed once in jeopardy, will never again know
rest. How typical of crime! Having given offence, it returns to its
source only to re-emerge with greater violence to compound its
fault.

FORWARD, MARCH!

Light *accents* the darkness, does it not? What of that first corner
of light, sculpted and thrust in limbo; its glare signaling distress; trying not to appear humble, yet twitching furtively across the loom of
gross and impossible obstacles. The light was a frightened mouse
unable to find its hole.

The vast gloom felt its own unbearable and burdensome weight,
while underneath and between, the broken web felt its breach; and
the stir that was not before brooded in the pit within the unending
waters.

Should not the light have snuffed itself out at its own effrontery?
But there was no stopping now! Time had jack-in-the-boxed out of
space. And what was that box itself, if not a prison for day and
night, and night by day, releasing and released by the other on an
endless wheel of flummery?

Founded on such gratuitous courtesies, the artifice of light was
nailed down, suspended and programmed by counterweights, in
response to … the COMMAND.

Part 2
CREATION + 2

The second night was closer to mercy. All was warmly at rest beneath velvet mantles, and comforted by melodic silences. Beneath the darknesses and over that part of the sea where light had never intruded, not yet, and even where the burning touch *had* been made; *the day had ended,* passed away, was no longer; that, in itself brought back the memory that had never been a memory before: peace.

But there were seams at the edge of the night. A spy was loose! A tightening pulse of tension. Not yet alarm. Quivering harp sounds as the rising wind blew through the strings.

It was nothing! The fearful expectancy dissipated. It had been nothing more than the soft and modest aftermath of twilight; apologizing, even with a faint red and gold blush, for its intrusion.

Yet, now the door is opened again! Who invited this soft-hued guest? Look at it now, brushing aside all the deep tints in the eastern corner, and adding gray gauze to the shadows ... all feather-brushed so painlessly that who would have suspected that from that same entrance would later emerge that coarseness, powdered and rouged in harlot colors; with a flounce: the dawn!

A blare of saxophones; and what had been oozing and filtering through the heavy muscles of thick clouds, sly and subtly invading the inner realm, now opened up and began raining down in crystalline streams of white flame.

The night was vanquished.

Part 3
TERRA INFIRMA

The miraculous intervention had wound up on its springs and, wagging its tail back and forth with unflagging optimism, conquered the endless darkness with intervals of illumination. Yet even the lashing of Day to the back of Night was, at best, a *praeludium*, a pre-climactic and anticipatory display of titan forces ... going where? Hail what destiny?

Specks were rising on the sea.

Under the arched horizon, huge swirls of water sucked downward in a turbulence of descending circles. Out of the hole in the depth emerged a tumescent swell that formed a strange scab as it surfaced, not of nebula, nor of ice, without flame.

The gall of it! Trespassing, taking up its tenancy on the body of the oceans, leprous, cancerous growth, truculently proclaiming victory when there had not been a battle.

Land, so called. It erupted on the neck of the proud seas ... and the waves kept rolling back, retreating, allowing dispossession by that which sucked and ingested, absorbing within itself that which was not its own.

The scab dried and grew hard. So soon after the COMMAND— the incredible image of all the oceans, bound-up, confined!

The natural order had been violated. Henceforth, there would always be contrast and comparison: the anti-state. Added to the dilemma of light against dark was the new one of sea against land. Is it surprising that with such tactics as ravage and retreat, recoup and reroute, the natural order became—War!

Now grown aware, seething in its depth, shaking its shoulders angrily, a huge mountain of water rolled back and looked forward with contempt, its waves peaked with writhing claws of foam. The menacing growl became a mighty roar; a challenge of bull's horns, momentum upon momentum; racing forward, heedless of restraint—a stupendous onslaught!

But ...

The land became rock, the rock became mountain. The enormous fists, the horns and spears and shouldering waves, cascaded together, beating at the barrier over and over again, only to be smashed into rainlets of spray ... into teardrops of helpless rage.

Thenceforth, and forever again, before charging in assault on the land, first each wave bows its head....

Part 4
THE EARTH'S HAIR IS GREEN

Darkness is equality. Were there imperfections before the light? What was concealed within the folds of eternal night? The halo along the perimeter of the uprising land served to outline the stark insignificance of the bare and shifting sands. Nor did it end there. Chained and held apart, exposed to dismal skies; the once-free seas were forced to interrupt themselves against the sides of these gross hulks, incapable of rolling with a great sweep over the endless horizon.

If a child had wrought all this, one hand would have swept it away and started over again. But children ask questions ... they tend to be impatient.

Wait! The drama has only just begun. The tense air of expectancy has returned to haunt the wings, attending the cue, straining toward the Director's plan in the absence of a script.

This time, the COMMAND was more whimsical, entering with a lilt and a flourish. It was as if, leaning back and surveying the great canvas, especially the heavy grays, the ponderous conception gives way to frivolity. Enter the Beautician!

Wherever the soil lay bald and bare, green hair fluttered out of the follicles. Between the rocks, the first trees were set down on heavy trunks, linking branches in a forest of yellow, red, and dark green leaves: that's a good touch! On with the paint and the powder-puff!

An inordinate fertility now took place, bursting out with new forms, colors, and textures, covered with coats of furry moss, combed over with grass and laughing green leaves, with spectacular touches of flowers and fruits profusely laden in colorful bouquets. The wig was uniquely successful; concealing, beyond measure, the ugliness underneath (where death lay incognito).

Now, the *piece de resistance*! Ingeniously, lest it all come to naught, a secret regenerative force was hidden in the depths of a mere pellet called *seed*, whose astonishing function it was to give each end a new beginning; that is, to become active at the upper length of a full growth and precede decay with a new and fresh unfolding.

A fine invention! One which pays tribute to the error, the wrong turn, the false assumption that inspires a greater solution than would have been possible without challenge. Think of it! Without the seed, each blade of grass would need to be newly created. This speculation in cyclical self-renewal transforms the scene entirely, making all the difference between 'game' and 'burden' for a harassed Creator. Imagine the first leaf continuing to rise upward without cease. Without this cycle, what a breviary of COMMANDS! It's not easy to be God."

Part 5
WITH FEET OF CLAY

Time was on a four-day romp into existence. Yet, the newness
was taking foothold alongside the ageless of forgotten origin and
within the unseen boundaries of space that would seem eternal until
one wondered about the before.

A little bit of elbow and shove, a stretch, a bulge; a discovery of
new space ... already, it wore that air of inevitability, the illusion that
it had aged prior to its own conception.

Springs uncoiled as tensions began to ease; the oceans loafed
around their fences while the dark clouds drifted and yawned, dissipated into loose and tiny puffs, and the sun lazed toward its zenith.

But the Sabbath was not yet!

First, a wheeze. The earth groaned, feeling the burrowing flame
within its bowels. impossible pain! The earth heaved, and squeezed,
quaking open a furnace, a cauldron of transforming flame. The entire
universe balanced its fear, trembling as the burrowing eye of flame
within the earth's intestines expelled liquid bursts of clay and fire.

As the soft clay hardened, became gelatinous; shook back and
forth with its own inner force, visible within the depth was a curious transparency of eyes and legs, bones and flesh, tail and torso ...
more intimated than revealed.

Surely, none of this had ever been before. Yet, the question asked
itself: to what purpose, the clay? Since nothing in Creation is for
naught.

But the explanation was more obscure than the question....

After the winds had trumpeted through the clouds and the last
moanings of the earth had subsided; as the sea held back its waves,
and waited; while the sun and moon stared back with wide-apart
and diffident eyes; while the entire universe sucked in and waited ...
the tip of His finger touched the clay!

The balls of clay began to spin in a merry-go-round whirl, a *gross-*

er fugue of centrifugal force. It became a madly hilarious game. A potter's wheel, spinning, smoking, translating the clay into form and incredible substance: a menagerie of animals, insects, birds and fishes, came thumping, winging, swimming, crawling into existence.

The clay became skin, grew hair, or, formed scales and hard shells to shelter, cover, protect and keep warm the precious network underneath of veins and entrails, metering the blood, routing a circular dance to the thud beat and pulse, where the cycle begins and ends in its own unique and living heart.

Hark, the exclamation mark!

All in all, it was a monstrous agglomeration; a riot of life given to all forms and conditions of clay without reserve in an orgy of the imagination. Nothing discarded! Spared, the aberrations of fancy: the nose of the elephant winding around the neck of the giraffe. Spared, the inequalities and injustices: after all, why *should* the serpent stand tall and princely and already wise while the turtle, through no fault other than concept, needs to grovel on its belly, never free of its prison?

Moreover, without regard to blunders, deformations, or unsuitability, without confession to a single fault or loose error, to each and every one was granted that other miracle of cyclic self-fulfillment: the Seed. All was now perpetuated. Never could a lamb hope to give birth to a wolf!

Night was ebbed; the sea, chained between mounds of land under the tight-stretched sky, huge green leaves waved without meaning; bearing fruit to fall foul within the sweating grass.

Now, these strange and stranger emanations of clay!

Fish, swimming in circles, blinking foolishly; insects, crawling in stupid profusion, colliding in confusion; birds, taking flight to nowhere. Over the face of the earth, hordes of animals roving and roaming, roaring and rearing at the sight of one another.

So far, the clay had given testimony that when space assumes form, it requires substance to complete itself. But what is substance without meaning? It does not suffice. This living clay! Alive to what? Filling space, for what reason? Why? Why? The entire universe sat powerless in judgment, waiting ... Meaning!!!?

Part 6
THAT BREATH!

Oh, those great and supple fingers! What have You wrought from the common clay, how high have You raised the dust? Caressing, modeling; taking Your time now; a somber *capriccio*, a study in Thy own reflection, the image not the source; yet, more than random sculpture. Further to conceit, lest it become neither more nor less than the *golem* of God, or, worse yet; the toy of the angels, He breathed the air of His own spirit into the vacuum between the layers of clay—and it was Man!

That moment when the clay became flesh, when the wide nostrils inhaled His breath; the entire hierarchy in Heaven thrilled and trembled; surpassed by the one who had participated in his own creation, filling his lungs with the breath which was to become the body and of the blood of God! It was within that moment that Lucifer lost his light and entered the darkness, and if there was commotion in Eternity, it was in the fear that what God had given so freely would dishonor Creation and raise a harvest of rebellion.

Of small moment now, the lineage of dust; the vegetable matter of fetid clay; not even the sacrifice of Lucifer brought flagrancy to court: exchanging, one with the other, the first one's light divesting the other's darkness. No claim could equal the breath, His Breath, that Breath!

He awoke!

He awoke, brushing the dust from his eyes; singing, while stretching his limbs.

He awoke! He touched ... fingertip to petal, soft, sensual rasp. *He looked* ... skyful of birds against the fires of sunrise (already wanting to fly; arms flapping empirically.) *He smelled* ...the cool and perfumed morning breezes, exhilarating and reviving the ecstasy of that first breath!

And he tasted and he heard and he felt the path of the breath winding its way, threading in and out of tissues, at once, responding with a pulse; welcoming the exhale of God through miles of intestines, convolutions of the brain; splashing inside the blood, while cells multiplied thirstily; blowing itself out, at last, inside the heart; absorbed, and rocking back and forth, contentedly.

Call the Dust-Come-to-Life Adam. Now, watch carefully! You've seen that breath enter the clay; the clay become flesh; housing its own spirit which is of the lost light of the deposed Prince ... now, see this! The arms jerk; the legs kick; the lips twitch and turn from blue to red. Now, the great hulk rises, exulting in plenitude. That breath has reached the heart—the drum beats!—Here it comes! ... *the exhale!* Give witness here, dare the sight, if you can! Man is returning the breath! It can be heard rasping against the lungs, a long, subsiding exhale, there it is, flung out of the body, like an invader. But he can't! He can't do without it! See how he sucks the air, bites it between his teeth—can't do within it!—must go begging back the breath: in-out, in-out, in-out, learning to live with it, panting now, gusting winds through his system; now, tentatively trying to do without breath, gasping; then, bursting open with the ballooned intake.

Thus, was the man fitted to the breath; and joined loosely to his Creator. How loosely would be seen again and again as the breath settled in; and, once more, the arms flapped experimentally, the heart thumped, the blood boiled over, and man stood poised over high and higher launching platforms, readying the spring over and beyond the arc of the intervening skies. *Oh, that breath!*

Part 7

THOUSANDS OF EARS

"I!"

The lone word was its own wilderness; an alphabet of meaning, the sum total of which, added to a string of zeros, still must conclude with *one* ... plus pride, plus defiance, minus the capacity to love ... Satan, of course.

Jesus was within himself, feeling his way toward insights, seeking to comprehend the ways of Satan and the compulsion of souls toward that web. Satan, however, had done his own penetrating.

"Is it *I* who substitute the glitter for the gold?" Satan fished out the substance of Jesus' meditation. "You wonder why a man would barter with me ... why would he trade his own sweet repose and forever green fields for the frenzies of the flesh; the intoxication of the senses?

"You turn away from the sensual cleavage of day from night; you deny the visual evidence, without blushing, the lewd tumescence of land rising between the mother seas ... and yet *you* would give evidence about creation?!

"What is it that hovers over all this, unleashing COMMANDS like thunderbolts? What is above the flesh and the spirit, yet parleys with both? What, above all, defines the highest development, the ultimate maturity?

"I expect a static reply: God ... but that answer is not in motion; it confuses meaning with definition; doesn't dare approach the source, the root laid bare. Before you leave this wilderness, Jesus, you will see all the sands of the desert form the secret name, the One that transforms Will into Truth and writes the last history: **Power!**"

This was Satan's time. Preliminaries usually are. The flesh is yet on the bone, bidding fair to become a cadaver. "Shall we dispense with pawns, Jesus? King against king. Queen against queen. Let's edit out all those humble, poor-me poses that are contradicted by your ambition. Also, by all means, let's furl up that frayed and muddied banner proclaiming 'Son of God.' Be *different*. There are just too many unemployed messiahs treading the earth with bare feet, wearing that blotched and rusted crown. You see me standing here, one foot tapping, the other quivering; even the bristles of my beard are pointing your way, looking to you for a genius of wit and parable; the extraordinary! The miraculous! Instead ... an ordinary saint is also so favored; plain, unsavory, unspiced and unflavored.

"What *is* it about you? *I'm* not at all impressed. *I* was not invited to your baptism, nor would I have come *here* were I not summoned. But *why?* You may or may not suspect this, but I do maintain a routine watch on every one of David's descendants. More peripatetic than prophetic, if you must know. Yes, Jesus, among my meanderings, I was in your wake at the Jordan. Until that moment, you were slightly suspect in my eyes ... a slim dossier of birth legends, something about a star and a ... stable? Put it down to myth-making. Then, there was that exhibition in the synagogue at your *bar-mitzvah* (precocious!), the constant mutterings in the fields, and your father's carpenter shop. The only important clue: a seeming reticence around women (in common with dedicated eunuchs). What does it amount to? Nary a distinguishing feature: without mole or birthmark. Far be it from me to mock a good carpenter. Haven't I already made my point that Creation could have used another nail! But, don't misunderstand me: nothing, not one genuine sign ... just a lone white lamb forever at pasture, counting the stars (incidentally, how many?).

"All at once, a commotion! From every corner of Sheol they kept shouting at me: 'He's off to be baptized!' Some, I suspect, entertained strange hopes. Jesus! Jesus! Jesus! I confess I knew less about you than some of my own. I had to calm the flames. I remember saying, 'After all, *he* is not doing the baptizing.'

"As for that wild man John, I had stopped paying him any mind for some time already. Routine surveillance only. I tend to consign these lone voices in the wilderness to Balaam's Ass. Perhaps, I should know better -but his head was already pledged.

"As it was described to me, there you were, immersed to the waist, the baptismal waters dripping down your upraised face, luminous, the ecstasy shining through your closed eyes. And then! The universe stopped turning, completely stopped, while a white dove hung suspended in mid-air over your head! Was it true that the instant was frozen into eternity? Was that *His* voice? Thousands of ears were raised (mass delusion?) as He called you by name, not a name reserved for patriarchs or prophets: neither Abraham nor Moses heard themselves so called, in all the hierarchy of angels, not one was thus honored ... *nor Lucifer!* So now, I look at you, the one He called 'My Beloved Son,' and dare not mock the challenge ... I look at you, and ask:

"*Are* you the MESSIAH?"

Part 8
OASIS

Plainly, Jesus was in anguish to the depths of his soul; having no choice but to listen to Satan expound on light against darkness, the land against the seas. The very spirit of Creation had been brought to trial! And Jesus wept. He was now well into his fast; and the cry came forth from his suffering body: "The hunger, the thirst are naught to bear against thy forked tongue dipped into my sustenance!"

Satan smiled and looked pleased. "How long can you look into the sun?" he retaliated on a cryptic note. "Do my images offend you ... burn too deep, touch the sensitive flesh? The most painful of all are new premises that shake you out of one world into another. The eyes become accustomed to darkness, Jesus. Take heart. You will see. Black angels, even. The other side of your imagination."

He took a flask out of his pocket, raised it up high, and shouted, "I give you a toast ... to the truth that dares!"

Of course, Satan knew that he was torturing Jesus at a time when his thirst was hardly bearable. He threw back his head several times, drinking deep, with gurgling sounds from the bottomless flask, each time, making a ceremony of wiping his lips and staring at Jesus with shining eyes. "Because it's desirable, doesn't make it sinful!"

With a sudden motion, Jesus threw himself on the ground, beating the earth with his fists. The pain was visible throughout his body, ending convulsively with tears.

Satan drew back, discreetly regarding the suffering form with distaste, and a slightly visible superior smile. All over, he thought. And so soon. Satan felt elated; but disappointed that what could have been a monumental game of chess had ended so soon. The full measure of his contempt was in the act of emptying his flask in the sands before Jesus' head, so that it spattered over his cheeks.

Jesus raised his head, and his soul was in that outcry, "Have pity on man!"

"Pity!" Satan picked it up, pretending to examine it between his fingers.

"Pity!" Satan juggled an imaginary trio of balls.

"Pity!" Meanwhile, Satan's mind had been in furious motion, recognizing that he had miscalculated. "Have you no pity for yourself?" Those tears were not for himself. What had stabbed the heart of Jesus that moment was the terrible vision of how *man* was vulnerable, a creature of desire under a hovering doom. This was to be the first step out of the wilderness toward the world of men. The mission was becoming clear.

Jesus raised his body until he was on his knees and doubled over in prayer, a figure of total humility. This he had sensed upon his first steps into the desert; that he was to become an intercessor; that an immense burden was upon him. Before the desert, it had been a matter of studious concern that he protect and preserve the rarity of holy love between himself and God. Now, the vast entanglements and unsprung traps of the outer world were waiting, surmised and verified by Satan's personal appearance, and his assault on the fundamental concepts of Creation.

"Stay God within me!"

Satan concealed his frustration by focusing on his impressive score of victories. He watched Jesus at prayer and with an ironic twist, visualized the pose as one of supplication; Jesus, on bent knees, pleading for his lost soul. Satan allowed himself a few moments of delight in his fantasy, then interposed jocularly,

"Chapter? Verse? Come, my rabbi: are you praying for or against me? At least, instruct my ears, that I might be tempted. Isn't that why we share these forty days?"

Jesus looked up to Satan with a deep and questioning glance, but what he found there was only mockery and endless contempt. Yet always would Jesus respond to the least note of hope, or sign of repentance! Always! There was that in Jesus that never failed to yield fruit from the least nourishment; and he responded to Satan's vaguest hint, taking him to pasture in those Psalms that touched on the labor of Creation:

"The heavens declare the glory of God, the vault of heaven

proclaims his handiwork; day discourses of it to day, night to night hands on the knowledge. No utterance at all, no speech, no sound that anyone can hear; yet their voice goes out through all the earth, and their message to the ends of the world High above, he pitched a tent for the sun, who comes out of his pavilion like a bridegroom, exulting like a hero to run his race. He has his rising on the edge of heaven, the end of his course is its furthest edge, and nothing can escape his heat ... "

Here, Satan chimed in, like a schoolboy proving to his Rabbi that he knew the lesson.

"The law of Yahweh is perfect, new life for the soul; the decree of Yahweh is trustworthy, wisdom for the simple. The precepts of Yahweh are upright, joy for the heart; the commandment of Yahweh is clear, light for the eyes. The fear of Yahweh is pure, lasting forever; the judgements of Yahweh are true, righteous, every one, more desirable than gold, even than the finest gold; his words are sweeter than honey, even than honey that drips from the comb. Thus your servant is formed by them, observance brings great reward. But who can detect his own failings? Wash out my hidden faults ... "

At this point, Satan emitted a long expiring sigh; shaking his hands loosely, simulating fatigue and utter boredom. Jesus completed the Psalm alone:

And from pride preserve your servant, never let it dominate me. So shall I be above reproach, free from grave sin. May the words of my mouth always find favor, and the whispering of my heart, in your presence, Yahweh my Rock, my Redeemer!"

Part 9

HOME

"Is it not written that pride goes before destruction?" Jesus asked of his tormentor. "Seek below for the haughty ... "

"Wait! Wait! Hold on there!" Satan came on aggressively, waving that away with a flourish of his arms. He leaned back, surveying Jesus with naked contempt. "Not only the proud ... *everybody* falls! Both the wise and the foolish! Saint and sinner, both! To rise is to fall! That loud crash you hear is what's going up, coming down: smashed, burst open—better not to have risen! Look! Look! See them all shaking their heads; watching and not believing their eyes. What confusion! The whispers! Tongues clucking! There it is ... sorrow? No! Joy! Joy! Joy! Looking like sorrow! And why all this ceremony? Look who has fallen! The one above the rest, the aloof one, the one parading sinlessness. He! He! He! Fallen! Down with the rest! A splash in the heap! The longer way down!"

Satan swirled like a top in an ecstatic circle, finishing with a leer, "At least I have this to say: my bottom has already bottomed!"

How does one find words for the Cynical One; the one totally abject without hope; the one who doesn't dream? Satan, once Lucifer, had lit up the heavens ... how does the light feel to One who was not always blind? Can the eye reverse itself?

In the absence of faith, Satan's premise seemed inviolable. After the purity of that first vision, once the eye becomes experienced, innocence must, indeed, give way to despair.

The sum of the difference was in Jesus' reply. Even the ring of his voice, surging youthfully, was a contrast to the dry, rational cadence with which Satan knocked on the doors of the flesh. "Satan, have you watched the child cease crawling, daring for the first time to walk upright? Were you that child once? The first time you fell, did you know that His eyes were on you? Did you feel the glow of love above you? Did you recognize Whose strong and tender arms were raising you to your feet again? God responds! Love gives love ... "

Satan stamped his foot, then jumped up and down before Jesus to get his attention. He cocked his ear, and asked contemptuously, "Did I hear you say God responds?" He guffawed, and shook his head. "Then, tell me this: What *strong*, what *tender* arm lifted up the Prince of Light when he tumbled into the darkness? Who was it that unlit the beacon? What sun and what moon shone in my stead? Who was it that bound me away from the sky? *With what love*?!"

For the first time Satan did not turn away from his own suffering; letting it swell out so that Jesus could see it with tears like pus, and the skin wrinkling through the mask, quivering with pain. Even the surface of it was enough, intimating an incredible depth.

Jesus drew back from the horror of it; but Satan followed him, thrusting his face obscenely near, shouting hoarsely, "*I* fell! And he turned his backside to me!"

He mocked Jesus' voice, "Tell me: what is the price of redemption today!?"

With one word, Jesus replied, "Desire."

Satan turned black and exploded with rage. "Could that be why you are here? To REDEEM SATAN!"

On his lips it sounded like the grossest heresy. Coming out of shock, he whirled around Jesus, spitting and grinding his teeth in a fury of hate and disgust. "Am I to be the Prodigal Son?" he roared at the sky, as if the thought was a sword and he was slashed to his depths by it.

He drew back his shoulders as if to release a physical bond, then, almost in delirium, bellowed his anguish, "Have you come to unbind me? To take me HOME?"

The last word echoed with the force of revelation. Satan clutched at the air suddenly, as if to draw it all back within, out of sight and locked up, even from himself. But there it was, with all it implied, fluttering out of reach like an escaped bird. HOME!

Jesus had gasped, immediately perceptive of all the implications in that one tragic note. He could feel the heat of Satan's eyes moving restlessly over his face, prying, seeking a sign that Jesus had understood.

In one instant, Satan's cause had become extrinsic. Whatever form or purpose that would seem noble in the guise of revolt, now became comic, a series of adolescent pratfalls punished by expulsion. The drawn-out silence was its own comment: the next act must be different; a new balance of character was now inevitable.

For the moment, Satan let go any pretense to the status of royalty, albeit, his heritage from the former Prince of Light was indisputable. Somehow, the first unchastened cry of revolt reverberating throughout the entire universe, seemed small and unheroic in this sudden glare: a nibbling at the heel, a buzzing annoyance, no more. The old scars ulcerated merely at the image that he and Jesus were obverse symbols of adoration for a high and mighty and unapproachable Deity. To have sacrificed all for that!

Trapped by his own ambivalence, Satan turned his hatred and scorn fully on Jesus. Under his breath, he vowed to grind this saint to dust and throw it into the winds. Prodding his memory for other ways to torture Jesus, taking great pleasure in the prospect; he turned to him, wishing to visualize the flame and extrapolate the writhing and shrieking around the actual person, only to be stunned by what he beheld!

Jesus had heard the word with which Satan had unclothed himself. He heard within and beyond the content of the word itself, heard the cry of the lost child within the beast; that touch of sadness behind the blasphemy; that flicker of longing where love seems no longer possible, and it all hung on a miraculous instant; long enough not to be an illusion, yet so rare that only the thought that it was possible would make it visible at all. Nothing less than the sanction of desire and the blessings returned from the furthest reaches of faith could give it credence. *There stood Jesus with open arms; stretching his hands out toward Satan with the deepest yearning!*

That Satan—the first Sophisticate—should stand rooted where he was, mouth open and dribbling, utterly confounded; that, in itself, was incredible. "It must have been rehearsed by God!"

Satan gasped inwardly, unable to conceive another with sufficient gall to attempt it. In his current state, he could not help at least some form of response, even drawing forth a surge of pity, unpracticed in the open, for the passionate and hopeless lover who thought to bring him *home.* For awhile, he studied the tiny points of light in Jesus' eyes, obviously ready to blaze up in great joy. He sensed the magnetism at the tip of Jesus' fingers, thinking loosely, suppose he had touched it! Somehow he had retrogressed to that unoccupied time when bravado was not yet revolt; and he could empathize genuinely toward that state where innocence was not yet in the balance....

Even so, Satan spoke with an assuredness that veered on contempt, "Jesus! Jesus! How do I enlighten thee! What is, *is*! If God were in Sheol, it would still be Sheol. Understand me when I say: the perfect states merge, no matter how you separate them! Put me in chains! Better still, and more incredibly, side me with God, destroy Sheol forever, with all its imps and demons and evil saints. The night gives way, but never ends! Don't you see it, Jesus? We, too, are within the miracle of cyclic self-fulfillment! Evil is it's own seed!"

Satan need not have spoken. Jesus had heard him within the sinking of his heart; yet, still he took a step closer. "Our Father," Jesus said, and the our was the embrace Satan had kicked away, "Our Father is gracious; He loves without end; and He forgives. Seek thou His kingdom again, Satan. He will not turn His eyes from thee."

The butterfly had lost one wing, and plunged. "Even me?" Satan asked with a mocking excessiveness of emotion. He had regained command, reverting to debonair poise and bourgeois pleasantries. All the while, however, he kept careful watch on Jesus from behind half-closed lids, roving eyes glinting and searching an advantage.

Still, Jesus kept his arms open, to Satan's embarrassment. "In the way of every path stands an altar. Merely that it exists, and is visible to those who turn that way, offers hope for the weary traveler. Yet, there are many that turn their backs to the altar, and depart; not believing, or believing it was not meant for them. There are those who come in hunger to steal from the altar, only to find that they are invited guests: that here, they end hunger forever. *What do you seek that is not already given to you?*

"There are those who know the penance of thirst, having lost the clear stream in search of the vine, returning whence they started to find the wine-filled chalice already on the altar. There! It stands before you! Give your pittance, but give freely. Make thy offerings pure; without the bitter grimace of the conquered; nor should you hope for threefold gain when a hundredfold is forthcoming. Let it be given in depth; even the pearl of smallest value, but that it comes from the heart. Come in peace; come bearing the whole of thy being; come singing; be contrite. To ye who make no bargain, to ye, I say: He who sends a lamb to God will see a flock return. Be truly penitent, drown thy sins: the past is behind thee. Not one of ye shall regret what, of yourselves, you have given; for ye shall know why you were born; and on what carpet, the road to eternal life. With pride and beaming with love, your Creator awaits you. Welcome!"

Never before had it been so quiet in Sheol.

CHAPTER THREE

FALLING STARS

"What has Adam lost, losing Eden?

Endless peace, yearning endlessly for contrast;

eternal life, eternally dull ...

a sword plunged into the hilt, never withdrawn."

—*Satan*

Part 1
THE FIRST TEMPTATION

The next time that Satan came upon Jesus, he saw a lean cross of darkened flesh outstretched in the desert sun. A knowing smile came over his lips; and he stood apart, studying the prone form; without disguising his disdain.

Jesus heard the voice in his ear, soft and gurgling: "No matter when I arrive, you're chewing prayers between your teeth ... and the words are like ants on your tongue. It's kind of a disgusting habit, you know. And I still can't understand why the spirit devours its own flesh ... why it's such a *mitzvah* to pull joy out of life, like a rotten tooth. Huh?"

Jesus forced himself to rise; watching Satan through a haze of sleep; rubbing his eyes, swaying to his feet, aware that one does not sleep in the presence of such a guest.

Satan watched dispassionately, taking note of those burning eyes in hollowed clefts, straining upward ... parched lips, black and swollen; loosely sewed together; sticking, unsticking with dried-out mutterings. Now, Jesus was bowing his head to the east to bless God for the new day that was fast approaching.

Most enervating of all was not the absence of food or drink; nor even that Satan kept appearing unexpectedly, disregarding day or night; so that he could never be fully at rest. Beyond the urgencies of the wilderness, beyond the demands of the living body, and the growing voice within his spirit that presaged his mission was the assault of sin. It came like knives on all parts of his body. And then there were the traps of the night, the slips of tongue, the hidden poisons, the more subtle forms of pride, the easy entrances with their not-so-easy exits. At one point, in the earliest hours of morning, Jesus was heard to cry out in terrible anguish: "Only Thou, God! Thou, alone!"

The next morning, Satan saw how loosely the flesh hung on

Jesus; sagging flaps of a tent between jutting bones, saw, and specu-
lated upon that translucence of skin through which the sun was filtering, illuminating the place of the spirit within. In that moment,
Satan was charmed by the miraculous sinlessness in the faith of Jesus
... and to that challenge, he rededicated himself.

Now, Satan bent down and drew a circle on the ground that
enclosed both himself and Jesus. "Don't let me disturb your morning devotion, Jesus. You're staring at the circle? It's just a device to
keep us together. Isn't that why we're here?"

Satan fumbled inside his pockets; then brought out a leg of lamb,
well roasted, and a leather pouch of wine. He looked at Jesus, smiling out of the side of his mouth.

"You know that I maintain a certain reputation for subtlety," he
announced, holding the lamb near Jesus' nose, while he nibbled at
it. "However, I never fail to be surprised at how successful a little
crudity can be!"

He threw back his head and squeezed wine in a stream into his
open mouth, swallowed, and wiped his lips. "Of course, subtlety
often defeats itself." Between nibbles and drinks, he went on: "I
would imagine ... however ... that the most formidable pressure ...
is on ... the one tempted ... Imagine! The digging, the roundabout
searching for reasons not to resist temptation. Speak of acrobatics!
Such forays of pure genius! That's why I try not to confuse ... the
appetites of the flesh with the hungers of the spirit. The flesh starves
itself out of existence: good riddance! The spirit, however, hangs on,
survives its container and retains its smell like a dead fish."

Jesus was not very steady on his feet; still he managed to step outside the circle, to the amazement of Satan. "Who are you, Jesus of
Nazareth? Who are you that I see legions of angels in your wake?"

Jesus gave him no heed. Again he was on his knees in an attitude
of prayer. "Thanks to Thee, Lord; that Thou hast granted me
patience in the face of evil; and strength beyond my burden. Thou
fillest my sight in the darkness of night when the abomination is
upon me. And my heart is overwhelmed."

Satan was not amused. The bone of the lamb had dried its marrow; and the wine returned to seed. "How shall I define thee, Jesus

ben Joseph ben David ben Adam ben Adonoi. Ben Adonoi! Look at
yourself, crusting in the desert; keeping a fire burning with indi-
gestible prayers, tortured like a dog, holding faith like a bone
between your teeth. Jesus, you can put on a wig and pretend to be
Samson; but Jesus, let me tell you something: Even Samson! He's
bald! A wig fools nobody. You are cursed! You have been made vulnerable to *Man*!"

Satan drew back, as real horror rose in him. "Save yourself!"

To this, Jesus made reply. Notwithstanding his meek and humble
look, the quiet assurance with which he spoke was almost as shattering as what he said. His eyes never left Satan's face. "Had it not
been for thee and thy craft, how would Adam and Eve, how would
man be turned aside from his Creator? Who would choose death for
thy false wit except for thy genius? How hast thou gardened the
seeds of sin! To know thee is to plead for justice in mercy to the ones
taken unaware of their choices; to beg for forgiveness for those who
stray and are lost unto themselves... How else turn away the just
wrath of God?"

"Wait! Before you get on your knees again..." Satan roared with
indignation. "I, too, have eaten the fruit of the Tree of Knowledge!
Or didn't you know? The sea is greater than its bed! When all the
waters become one wave!"

Suddenly the bourgeois pose fell apart in a roar of thunder, and
all of the visible Satan was a pillar of flame; and he was his own furnace. "The fault, I say, was itself: Creation!"

Just as suddenly, and without preparation, there was the slightly
pompous and overweight pose of the bourgeois again; wiping his
forehead and making the mild comment, "You would agree, I'm
sure, that faults grow larger in time. Even first faults!"

Jesus' reply was more than an abstraction. "The flesh can be
humbled," he said, "and the will of the spirit made accessible to the
One who gave it free rein to wander and waste itself before returning Home. There are those children who would almost want to
stray; upon seeing the tumultuous joy of the Father when the lost
one returns."

Satan's eyes twinkled. "The small fish fill the nets," he commented, snapping his fingers contemptuously. He looked down on Jesus haughtily. "I have considered the ruse that keeps me here with you in the desert, ungainfully employed ... while back there at the gates of Jerusalem, the one who calls himself the Messiah enters through the gates with most regal panoply. Am I wrong?"

Jesus was not to be trapped so readily. He replied obliquely, "Where you seek the One, there are many. And the gate through which they enter is not the one you scan. It has a name: repentance."

"Ah!" Satan retaliated with a mocking flourish, bowing from the waist. "That, I cannot concede! Speak if you will of unclean spirits, demons, furies, satyrs and succubae, all of these there are, but ... only one Satan!"

He looked off in the distance, shrugging his shoulder. "One Satan. One Messiah. One carpenter's son?" He arched his eyebrows quizzically.

"The many of us are the ones God loves," Jesus replied fervently.

Satan laughed, turning good-natured, "I'd like to pursue all this with ceremony, breaking bread and with a tiny glass of chilled wine to ease it down. But you would say I was tempting you, as if Heaven was not its own temptation. Not even a small, the smallest piece of cheese? No? No! Your senses salivate on upper ambrosias. Imagine dining without heavenly choruses! Such sensuality!"

Satan's amusement was such that he actually broke out into rollicking laughter. Then, seeing that he laughed all by himself, he stopped. "Yet, I'll agree, a crumb ends a fast as well as a banquet. The question is one of choice: which sensuality? But, choose! Why must you insist on the martyr's portion? How does one feast on martyrdom? Is there a sensuality in this that I haven't considered?"

Now Satan made a grand display; carelessly tossing away his half-chewed bone of lamb; then, spilling what remained of the wine over it. "Into the dust for the dogs!"

He leered in Jesus' face. "Yet, why should you be less favored than they?"

Jesus stared at the bone where it lay at his feet and, without a word, flung it away out of sight. As always, Satan took sustenance from contempt; recognizing that a master hand turns contempt into indignation and anger and, when your adversary is fully possessed by an extreme of emotion, he is exposed and vulnerable. So, Satan fed on the scene: "Bravo!" he exclaimed ironically. "Indeed, a pity!"

His eyes glinted with cruel humor; and he leaned forward like an outraged teacher addressing a dull student, "Let's suppose, admitting your torture, you had picked up the bone; studied it, licked the wine from the meat with the tip of your tongue ... bitten the tiniest piece.... What an example for Israel! Quick, spit it out! The *image*, I mean. Who would dare accuse you of being like anyone else, giving in a little? No, *you* must carve monuments to yourself—above God! After all, doesn't God confess His own sins; changing His mind, spitting out fire and brimstones?"

"Enough!" Jesus covered his ears; but Satan's voice had more than one entrance when he wanted to be heard. "How little you know your Creator!" Satan pursued his theme. "When He gave you His breath, he never meant you to choke on it, starving your body and drying it in the sun. Is it His pleasure, or your choice, Jesus of Nazareth? Wouldn't He prefer many more decades of daily prayers to this proud and heroic demise? You just don't comprehend the Word, and its living testimony. And the obstacle is pride: I mean pride that makes Satan humble by comparison. At least, I faced Him with my own image. Myself! But what is this guile that stands in His shadow as if He were a puppet of hidden fancies? Thunder and damnation, Jesus! What is your ambition? Are you protecting God?"

Jesus opened his lips to reply, touched to the quick by the succession of blasphemies, but he saw no audience in the face of Satan: at the moment, the haze of assumptions and gross distortions would have made it impossible. Yet he must address the clever lies at their source, exposing the point in the road, at least, where untruth wandered. "I am from my Father's house," he said, growing tender at the words, "His hand is over me." The last was said, not as a warning to Satan, but with such awe and humility that no one could have mistaken it.

What amazed Satan, however; that which he saw with genuine

surprise and incredulity, was the pity he found in the eyes of Jesus—
pity for him! And he who had wished to provoke Jesus to anger, was
himself provoked, flaring up on another course, "Now, it's my turn
to scribe tablets of stone with commandments! Something's wrong
with 'Thou shall' and 'Thou shall not' when the waters must rise
and the earth must quake to swallow up the best and the beyond.
I've seen with my own eyes the rage of jealousy and how He ravages
His own creation, defying logic and free will. Here! I take this grain
of sand on the tip of my finger. If I toss it into the void, and set it
spinning, it revolves, becomes the Earth! Now, put a tiny ant on it.
Oh, to put Creation newly into the seed! Could what will be grow
worse than what is?

"Stop blinding yourself with rainbows, Jesus! The truth is in
thunder and lightening, fire and brimstone, turning water to blood
and blood to water, murdering the first born. What work is this?

"Even if you are another Son of God, the beloved one who pleases Him, give heed once to what you will never hear spoken again. I
will speak to you of the anguish of God that He cannot be loved by
decree, only by desire. Why else free will! So you have a choice,
Jesus. You may be punished for making that choice, but then, to
choose freely is the true state of Adam. The knowledge of good and
evil is in it; and the evil is not to be free to choose.

"Who would not choose the unleashed joys of Sodom over the
severe and constrained blessed cities ... given a true choice! Who
would not choose the young and beautiful, the soft whores of Baby-
lon, over the gray-faced and seedless crows who glorify piety ...
given a true choice! Who would not rather dance with wild and fulfilled abandon, exhaling and inhaling His breath with ecstasy, rather
than lie inert in a prostrate pose that seeks to sanctify the already-
sanctified?

"The gloat and the bloat above the rattle in the throat. Jesus,
Jesus, Jesus, Yehuda of the Spirit, listen to me! I am possessed by the
moment! My eyes whirl and pierce like gimlets through the intervening skies ... I am Lucifer! Thou art Lucifer! Finally, the last of the
last and final judgments. Choose! Choose again, Jesus! Or, you will
be blinded by your own light!"

Jesus could actually feel Satan reading him, scanning his spirit, touching the fabric for flaws. He knew what Satan was looking for, and girded himself for battle; not as much against what Satan would offer, as the temptations of his own mission: that he would be drawn to lead rather than to be led by God.

Satan became impatient. Without waiting for any reply, he drew closer to the target. "Look at yourself, the portrait of death! Eaten up inside and out, drying in the sun with the figs and raisins. Insisting on the martyr's portion, your insides tightening, all ready to reject what hasn't been offered! That kind of confusion, I would say, is particular to the ones that mistake martyrdom for sanctity. Such confusion would be inconceivable with a reasonable and natural premise—for example, a full stomach turns away temptation. Isn't that better than, for example, if it gives pleasure it can't be good?

"Getting back to meat and wine, and the small circle of circumscribed existences ... do you have to qualify for bones in Heaven? Give an eye to yourself: what kind of prize is in that bony cage, more than a shriveled soul? There's no more than a pint of blood in you. This, you think I need in Sheol? Our saints have girth! Are merry! Their Eden has not even one restraint, and I'll tell you our secret ... two words ... self indulgence. With us, you come in with the tide, with us; every instinct grows high on the vine, and flourishes. We insist that nobody who enters has any regrets, or—horrors!—even conceives of begging for forgiveness. Yet, with all this which for you is anathema, I say this," here, he screwed up one eye and closed the other, "One day, you will come among us…"

Jesus shuddered.

"…unless," Satan continued, "unless you are the One, the One and Only spirit without sin. This I do not believe."

Immediately, Jesus recognized the last gate on the end of the path for what it was and where Satan's strategy was leading. He closed his eyes, not to look further on that fleshy face with its alert and greedy look and when he opened them again, he saw Satan lifting a long, narrow stone from the ground.

"Here, take this," Satan was saying to him.

"If you are the Son of God, tell this stone to turn into a loaf."

Jesus gave his reply to all that had gone before. His words were more than a skillful avoidance of the open trap; more than just a denial of negation. He affirmed the primacy of the search for light and the nobility of the soul. "Man does not live by bread alone."

Satan listened, sifting the words in his consciousness. He gave respect to Jesus with a slight nod; then added irrepressibly: "Yes. He also needs wine."

Part 2

THE LAST PERFECT DAY

The luxurious withdrawal of the Divine Presence for the Sabbath left the earth with such a sense of vacancy that it prompted a comment from the acerbic wit of the Serpent: "Was it truly a wedding, or, more likely, a divorce?"

The other living beasts, birds, insects and fish were not as finely tuned yet; still waiting to be named by Adam, so that the spice of the Serpent passed over their heads while they rummaged within themselves.

Patently, it was a time for orbits and cycles to wear into their routes; a time for feet and fins and wings to move in their sockets; a time to forage and explore and find family; accept, reject; taste and swallow; seek high and burrow low—in short, to footprint the soft soil, each to their own destiny.

And on that first day, it all worked!

It was Adam, most of all, who knew that God was not immediately there. He felt what was not yet fright; the sense of a curtain closing over his head. So far, his feelings had been quite simple; only one at a time; without shades, variances, contrasts or uncertainties. He turned easily from being sad, deprived of His immediacy, to feeling joy in his own will; that he was free to roam, free to find his own way, free to enthrone his own realm. If there had been a cradle, he would have climbed out of it; crawling, jumping, skipping along; examining his new world with insatiable curiosity, secure, and perfectly innocent ... It all worked! All the sciences, the laws of nature, the mechanical settings, the gears, the sockets, chemical formulae, mathematics, even the letters of the alphabets, all were there, intimating their brilliant array; awaiting discovery by the bearer of the *breath*.

There was a high bluff overlooking all of Eden. Without knowing why it seemed attractive to him, Adam reached the top; then he knew why....

From this vantage point, even the birds were beneath him; and the breath surged inside him, coloring his cheeks while he panted with excitement.

Just as he could see all of his world; so could he be seen by all that lived beneath him; and as they looked up; some, even mistaking him for their creator; called to him, "Adam! Greatness of Clay!"

And Adam saw that only he was without counterpart; being, without division, the fusion of male and female; and he felt proud, in the image of God.

Thus, Adam amused himself, giving names to all that lived and passed in review. Only the serpent demurred, rejecting the appellation *snake*; smiling, so that Adam would not take offence.

By this time, Adam had begun to tire of his apartness; and, feeling the urge to mingle, he descended into his own world, feeling pleased that the larger animals made way for him; that the trees bent over his way to entice him with their fruits. With his presence, the first sense of meaning emerged, even if only a distant focus of pending order and pre-orchestrated harmonies that signaled a paradise within the spirit. With fulfillment preceding its vistas, the accent was less on quest and discovery, more on participation. As yet, there was not a toehold for desire; nor did form allow function the least cause for frustration; and need had no impediment among all the congruities.

Without hesitation, with natural ease, the same tongue communicated with all the animals alike. Adam, standing in the midst of a collage of furry faces, feeling their warm and liquid eyes upon him; responded with a rush of his own emotions toward a good and gracious Creator who had made it all possible. Thus, Adam's first dialogue with the animals was a prayer, giving thanksgiving to God.

When the prayer was over, a long silence ensued while all together and individually, they communed within their own depths, joining their personal and precious insights to the mysterious and unthreatening vastness without. And for the first and last time, the entire world was united, free of any cause for protest.

From outside the circle surrounding Adam, long fingers touched Adam's cheeks, then pinched him affectionately ... enter the Serpent, showing his teeth in a broad smile; staring at Adam as if the act itself were consequential. Then, when the Serpent spoke, it was with an air of great significance, "Are you mated unto yourself?"

Hearing this, Adam stared and saw in a new way that each and every creature was either male or female. As the thought began to fill his mind, it crowded out his first insight: that he, alone, was in the dual image of God.

And when the Serpent asked further, eyes glittering with a hint of mockery, "And where will you bury your seed?" there came between them an uneasiness that affected all within hearing who were now taking note of each other's differences.

Adam noticed that his heart was beating more rapidly. The words of the Serpent had assailed his ears, knifing their way down inside his depths, giving him a taste of pain. Adam looked again; and in a new light, viewing all the animals in pairs, he invented a new feeling called loneliness; and this new feeling, dredged along with it a companion called sadness; and, together, they verged toward despair, the sum of both.

Adam stared back at the Serpent hard and fast, seeking a further clue, without yet beginning to recognize the extent of his dilemma.

It could not succeed however; not in the child Adam, within whom feeling and response were so closely joined. Nor did Adam have to study the way to give vent to his sorrow. He sat down on a rock; bent his body over, upper on lower; wrung his hands together, and like a primed pump, out flowed the tears! Once realized, his emotions came to the fore in crescendos of sobs and moans, punctuated by a sharp intake of breath at the beginning, and a railing and explosive output at the peak.

Watching Adam out of control, the animals turned to each other, confused and uncertain. They glanced sideward at the Serpent querulously, some even wondering if, after all, the Serpent was the dominant power. Mostly it was an embarrassing sight, seeing their erstwhile genial lord so bitterly unhappy; and they responded with as little guile as their master had shown; open and completely exposed; unvaccinated against impurity.

Adam stood up, and cried out: "I am a prisoner of my loneliness!"

What he said, perhaps, was too intense a reaction to the moment. With more time and distance behind him, he might have hesitated and recognized the experience; he might have been guided by the sense of his own destiny, as God had given it to him, he might not have reacted with such perfect innocence, there would not have been such a direct route available to his heart, nor would he have been wide open and so completely vulnerable.

Yet, who can say that Adam's outcry was not the true echo of God's own desire?

"Whence will my children come?" What had he understood already? It was clear that Adam was beyond the others; groping, reaching out painfully to a higher sphere that he, himself, was not fully aware of.

Was it an omission, God? An oversight, God? Where was Adam's seed, God? Where, in what soil, would it take root? Being in Thy image, did you mean him to bear Thy own and personal loneliness? Cyclical self fulfillment, God: what happened here?

Verily, the lamentation of Adam was its own commentary, a piercing coda to the jubilation that had been the Sabbath's opening chord. Adam's body rocked back and forth, seeking relief in motion. "Am I to be my own, and only, generation?" He pierced the intervening sky, each word, an arrow.

And He that was the father, listened and was silent, and so strong was the silence that it flung back all the arrows to earth with bent tips. But, who can know what is not to be known; except that He reveals it. Notwithstanding this nod of Faith; the silence of God came as a shock of surprise-fear-wonder-doubt, coursing through the invisible fibers of the eternal cosmos; setting them off vibrating like the strings of a great harp in the wind ... even the angels hung suspended.

That stir on earth was Adam. If the outcry had that within itself of the nature of child; also, it was a noble moment ... an exhalation toward his Maker, proving the unfettering of the will towards its own destinies; even away from the values of the Absolute.

Poor Adam! Struggling. Unknowing. Without a past. Without withal to anticipate. After all, what is stricture without scripture?

God returned a languid glance toward Eden. There was Adam, baying at the moon in a landscape of fixed mounds and moving shadows. And the child felt the tenderness within the darkness; saw himself at the other end of a giant eye, moist with love and comprehension; and, finally, he let his tears dry, and waited to be comforted.

And as God confronted His masterpiece; the end of a sigh was in the stillness of the wind. Adam; at the moment not lord of anything, least of all himself; was lying head down, open-mouthed on the breast of the earth ... as he awaited the mercy of God, lids of Adam's eyes grew heavy and curtained the without from the within. While he communed with the bread and wine of all beginnings where the flesh becomes spirit; while God shared with him the secret of the birth of the seed, Adam slept through the surprise of the opening of his flesh, where the rib rose like a monument before the event it celebrates, and it became clear that all time had awaited this moment ... and the seed that was there, divided itself; each part, the gold of the clay; each part, in permanent longing ordaining the new life, the inexhaustible generations that would rise from each reunion.

The mother was no longer in man alone, and there, where the rib had been ... and there, where the rib had gone ... was a sacred thrust, was a sanctified hollow, the repository of a dream; a dream that had burned itself deep inside the seed, over and over again to be transmitted through the generations. The dream was the secret that God had shared with Adam, and the secret was the substance of Eden, and the secret was a beacon for even the bleakest of nights, and that which was mother-father and father-mother to all that awaited creation, looked toward this rib, made a cradle for it, stared at the resting place; thrilled and flowing over with the secret—among all the births; out of any entrance; through one of these doors; one, among all children will be your Messiah!

Adam laughed in his sleep.

Part 3

TO DREAM OF LILITH

Adam had not yet awakened to that new self; further removed from the original clay. However, there it was, the atoms were exploded in the seed; separated, and magnetized with longing, to return to that prior interlocking which is perfect fulfillment. Henceforth, Adam-Man and Adam-Woman must complete the search and striving to return the rib to the gaping cave of the flesh. Which Adam retained more of the original breath of God?

Meanwhile, the sun and the moon moved in rapid constellation, aimless, while Adam luxuriated in the deep anesthesia of his surgery. The clay had been edited; the birth, revised. Still clinging, Adam remained joined to the umbilicus of that mystical adventure which had thrust him out of darkness, and he was loath to wake up.

"Adam. Come forth!"

Yet, he rested in limbo, the dream of a dream, his lips around a milkless breast, sucking, gaining naught. Then, riding the back of the serpent within sight of Lilith. She, who never was yet mates desire to fantasy; froth from ecstasy. And the taste of her who never was, while the serpent smiled, remained within the pools of his blood, reflecting ancient memories.

Adam had no wish to open his eyes and scatter the dream into unredeemable bits. Yet, he awoke with closed eyes. A stir was beside him, the sound of another breath. He turned on his side, stretching forth his arms languorously. His fingers touched, enjoyed the luxury of touch, cool and sculptured flesh. His arm grew stiff. Abruptly, he opened one eye. Then, in shock, the other!

He would have said, "Lilith!" The words were already forming. But, she who was himself, came to him first; saying those simple and portentous words: "I am your wife, Eve."

Adam leapt to his feet. Slowly and cautiously, he walked around Eve, keeping his distance. The other flesh cried out to him, magnetizing his feelings, but he kept his lips tight, unable to be indifferent to his mirror image, almost resenting the intrusion.

Into her eyes, probing: must I share with you? The question asked itself without rising to his lips.

Eve smiled easily, and her first words cut into the tension. "Have I always known you?" she asked. She held her face up to him, and her eyes softened, drawing him tenderly into her hope and yearning.

Still, Adam drew back, studying his senses.... Was this she? She, who would be wife and mother to his needs, friend and enemy, over whom he would rule and by whom be ruled, she, who would end and extend his loneliness? Without warning, his heart surged and opened wide its gates. Adam reached over, and touched her cheeks with the fingertips of both his hands. He sighed.

"Adam," she whispered, and his lips formed her name "Eve," without making a sound.

Already wise in her ways, Eve took Adam's hands in hers, pressing each finger in turn. And thus, Eden became Paradise.

Part 4
THAT TREE!

"Adam! Eve!" Who else spoke thus beyond their ears and within their depths, reaching through their pores to their innermost being, seeping beneath the sheaf that bundled the bone and flesh to their souls? They listened and gave heed to the word of God.

"You are not to eat of that tree in the middle of the garden, for with the knowledge of good and evil, you will surely die."

Amid all the wonders, they had, indeed, already beheld its majesty, but had lost sight of it among the plenitude of other miracles. But after God had spoken, they found themselves returning to the middle of the garden, that they might see it again in the light of the forbidden, and take warning.

It was the same tree they saw, strangely, however, not the same sight. Their hearts palpitated in the presence of their alerted senses. The longer they stared, the more it seemed that all mysteries were here united, that it had *been*, before Eden it had been. That when all that grew in Eden was still in bud; that tree was already as it was: pillar post and anchor joint for all the earth that held firm in the tight embrace of its roots; supporting an elaborate maze of convoluting branches and ivy growths, spanning a jungle between soil and sky.

During all its growth not a single branch had been molested by winds, or softened by the rain, nor within its pith had a single insect burrowed. It was pristine. Truly, a living testament to the immutable, this venerable giant from God's own orchard.

What else was to be seen was the ultimate homage; the display of gratitude to the Conceiver; that humble offering of boundless wealth at the end of every branch: medallions of fruit in which the first juices of the sapling intermingled with the matured wines, sweet with youth, rich with age and experience. Each stem still sucked sustenance from the first sun on the first seed and the flowers that betokened the fruit yet in birth made no secret of their laughter.

Within all that profusion, who would see, or take note of one missing strand? Yet, it was a magnet to the eyes of Adam and Eve, both looking up at the same moment to that one branch whose one stem was the only one without fruit. Was it conspicuous by the bent heads of its flowers or was it the silence in the midst of sound? The wound was there.

When the whisper dares its breath the name it speaks is ... Lucifer. He, whose trembling fingers reached out, touched, drew back, then, in one overwhelming moment, seized and pulled away the prize. Then, returned it in anguish to a stem that would not accept it—aghast!—not asking mercy, biting, the first time desperately, then one more bite and another, more easily.

He beheld that the sea was no greater than its bed at which the waves rose in revolt. And, on his lips, a new word was formed, which was to be the redeeming sign of the new dilemma. And the word was given power. And the power of the word was NO!

Thus, he who had been the son of the light became a child of darkness; both slave and master; learning the ways of revolt, and bringing sin into the world. The son had fathered temptation, illusion and self-deception, without which the despair into which he had fallen would have become unbearable.

There, in the quiet music of the twilight when the silences are long and well thought out, Eve turned away from the entranced vision of that tree, perturbed, as she pondered again what God had said. She turned to Adam with her question, "To die! What does that mean?"

Adam had no reply.

Part 5

CON WITHOUT PRO

What was it that brought Eve back, stopping to stare in wonder, fascinated by the muscles and sinews of that tree?

It would be too contrived to ascribe other than the simplest and most innocent form of curiosity to Eve's return; despite that she left Adam's side to do so, and, as might be inferred in retrospect, the soil was hot for the seed.

God's admonition still rang in her ears; and nary a question was in her mind to trouble her. At the moment, she was drawn to the tree as separateness: that from which all the rest were apart, that which eluded meaning. Nor did she seek to understand. As it had always been, and ever would be, it was there!

"Mistress of the earth!" it seemed to Eve that the tree spoke from within itself; and it pleased her, as did the bowed head of the lion when it passed before her. But then, from behind the trunk where he had been keeping watch, out stepped the serpent. He sidled up to Eve, smiling at her from under half-closed lids, impossible to ignore. He made her feel uneasy.

The words of the serpent pleased her, however. It would seem that his tongue moved on oiled hinges, with a glibness and rehearsed inflections that would have sounded warnings to a more sophisticated, less innocent ear. The small girl in Eve was gladdened.

"Do you gaze on your property?" the serpent asked with smooth warmth, and the respect of an inferior. "Look what God put in your hands! Beyond all that lives, at the end of every harvest, you are! Command and we obey! Reach out and touch your wealth! You are like God on earth, on earth, you *are* God!"

Eve smiled and listened, opening her heart.

"Just look at that tree," the serpent continued, "the fruit, bursting with juices—and secrets!" The serpent leaned over confidentially, and whispered, "His secrets!"

Eve shook her head, remembering God's warning.

The serpent also shook his head. "No, no, don't! Mistress, mistress! Please, not that!"

How could Eve mistake the mockery in the serpent's voice?

"One bite! Only one bite … and you have the key!"

"Key," Eve's eyes were glazed.

The serpent looked at her with open surprise. "Can you fly like a bird? Swim across oceans? Sound the thunder? Hold back the night?" The serpent did not wait for an answer, eyeing Eve shrewdly, he added, "But you are Mistress of the earth."

Eve returned his probing stare with a fatuous smile, not sure whether she should accept all this with some little embarrassment; or make light of the extreme edges on which the serpent rested his case.

"Except for the key …" Eve added wistfully.

"But it has your name on it!" The serpent looked at Eve with a full shock of surprise. "What good are all the doors to His mansion if never a key is turned in its lock? After all, you are His guest! He has made you at home, given you the freedom of His garden.... Must He hold your hand while you turn the key?"

"Not the fruit..." Eve said dismally, trying to pierce her confusion.

"But that's the price!" the serpent interjected. "Is God so simple that you can read him so easily, those times He says 'No' when "Yes' is what He hopes you will hear.... How can you bear His breath without being Queen?"

The serpent walked away, muttering to himself with disgust. Eve looked after him, upset at being abandoned with this dilemma; but, after a few paces, he wheeled around on his heels, shouting, "Command me! Command me to bring you the fruit from that tree! *I* can't refuse … command me!"

Eve stiffened; one eye on the fruit; one, on the serpent raising his hand toward it, dangerously close.

"Why must I obey?" the serpent asked, still keeping his hand suspended. "I obey the breath inside your flesh; the power that forms words on your tongue. Don't I know that being imitates its origins!

Am I so dense that I can't hear Him through you? And if you were to order me to bring that fruit to you, would I not bow my head and do your will, because the breath asks it of me? And it's your breath now, isn't it, which makes you your own Creator in the mystical sense, a piece of Himself."

By this time, Eve was floundering; looking at the fruit not at the serpent, then, in turmoil, turning her sight up the endless length of the tree where it seemed to pierce the incredibly blue sky.

The serpent followed her glance, and read her thoughts. "*He* has tasted the fruit. *He* knows good and evil and everything in between: what else is in the business of God, beyond separating light from darkness? But, that's up there! What about here on earth? Who else but His own likenesses! The anima *par excellence!* The heirs to His kingdom! How will you judge without judgment; not knowing whether good is evil; or evil, good? Can we, your subjects, depend on you? Can you take the route of kings and queens, deciding for yourself? Can you?"

Eve looked inward with trepidation.

The serpent bowed his head, waiting for Eve's reply; and when the silence became unbearably tense; he continued: "Oh, Adam; where are you?" When he saw, however, that Eve perked up at this suggestion, grateful for the reprieve, he veered off quickly to another route. "If it was Adam, standing where you are, he would have the fruit between his teeth already, sucking its juices. But tell me this, Eve. Were you only a piece of the rib, as they say? Did the breath also fill your lungs? I had thought you were two in one flesh … aren't you? Is it only Adam whose will is free? A king and no queen?"

The serpent's eyes bored into Eve; and now it all seemed like a dream, and the words entered her pores and would not sweat out.

"Isn't the drama pre-ordained? That I would be here, and you would come to me without knowing why? Do the waters have to be told to withdraw from the wet shore when the young moon beckons? Yes or no comes later, much later, knowing what is good and what is not. You, Adam who is Eve, your lips are moist, your teeth parted. I hear the pant of your breath, even without your tongue around it, I read your command, and obey my queen. The fruit is off the bough ... there! Now, bite!"

The voice of the serpent rippled with suppressed laughter. He made a charade of the bite and the chewing, "That your eyes may be opened, that you may be like God."

The fruit came off the bough, filling the cup of her hand while the stem wound round her finger: a wedding band. Her arm, a slow pendulum ending at her lips, pausing. "You are not to eat ..." came again the echo of Him. The toll hung suspended.

Meanwhile, the branch from whence the fruit was torn; shriveled and fell away. *That* tree bent its head, mourning, shaking its leaves, feeling the end of Eden. The cry of her seed; the kick in her womb; even, the sighs in the wind, never reached her ears above the serpent's flute octaves, "That you may be ..."

Eve bit the fruit. Her teeth were claws, sundering the skin, and the juices welled up and trickled, forming a stream now, cascading over her gullet, fully into the urn of her throat, sweet going down; bitter regurgitated. Thence, the curved-tooth-printed, half-moon of fruit, roller-coasted the rise and fall, the curves of her entrails, taking passage through her innards. In its wake, the sting never left her teeth, her tongue prickled and warped, never to be flat again and her throat contracted, forcing the next and last swallow.

That moment, Eve knew the force of a heartbeat; prodded by fear, exulting in power. And she held her hand to her heart, feeling the bird throb and pulse, wanting to fly. That moment, how could she know, the clock was wound, each second mourning the one that had passed, and would never be again.

Then, seeking the eye of the serpent, which had fled, she saw *that* tree again, shriveled and bare, peeling its bark open to the mites. Feeling the freeze on her flesh, she turned, and what she saw was foreign to before.

What had been crystal-bright, fearless night, laughing light was now gray and grime, filth and slime. All this that had been before, without flaw, now, exposed to the core, was black and bristly seen without love. A veil came between her eyes and the vision, an interpose of dark filters, making shambles of the light, cobwebbing the landscape, foreshadowing the spiders of evil.

In the cacophony of new sounds, the new 'reality' of the unreal, Eve entered into conflict with creation; seeing the pale and reflected, divisible from Eden.

She recoiled, complaining bitterly, "Why was I so innocent?"

That tree groaned, a distant lion woke from sleep, raised its head and moaned and Eve spoke to the same sky, "Truly, I am born again! But why am I naked?"

Part 6

DEPOSITION

The serpent returned, leading Adam by the hand.

Eve saw them emerge from behind a bush and was ashamed that Adam saw her in all her bareness. Yet she did not stir from where she had been rooted, and chose to ignore the glittering, inquisitive stare of the serpent. As for Adam, something more than a narrow stretch of time and the short arc of distance had come between them. Looking at him, she had the new and unfathomable sense of a voice within herself, the sign of an inner life, henceforth to influence and be inseparable from the days and nights of her self. The voice spoke only to the ear turned inward, "How callow is this youth!"

The bright and brimming eyes of Adam were on her face, taking joy at the first sight of her, and now there were two voices within her, one saying, "What did the serpent tell Adam?" and the other, mocking the soft smile spreading on his lips, "Oh, lamb! Oh, innocent!" Even as her thoughts indulged its more intimate sight; she could hear the serpent whispering, "If Adam does not bite ..."

BITE! Suddenly, she looked down at her hand, remembering. Adam, following her gaze, saw the fruit in her fist, a large bite already gone. He gasped. His eyes grew wide then closed.

Meanwhile, the serpent completed his thought, hissing " ...he could betray you to Him, or put you aside, or ..."

Adam opened his eyes again, licking his dry lips. When he could speak, one word came out of his lips in a drawn-out whisper: "How?"

Eve was pleased. Had he asked "Why?" she could not have replied with a clear conscience. But the serpent took the responsibility, "That she may be like God ..."

Adam let the words fall on his ears, not ready yet to comprehend what was being said. As yet, he had not absorbed the first and foremost fact: the fruit was in Eve's hand and yet she stood there! Erect on her feet! Visibly unharmed! Without indictment!

Pondering this and seeking no further what his mind could not encompass, he looked from the fruit in Eve's hand to *that* tree, almost expecting that the upward thrust of its limbs into the blue sky would provide an answer. No challenge came back. He saw the bough that had fallen and his eye hovered over it, surmising that this had been the one to provide fruit for Eve. He was fascinated by it, letting it take hold of his imagination. Where else in Eden could one find anything broken off and fallen away, wasting itself so uselessly? At the same time, it would seem to be pointing a brown and crooked finger right at him, as if directing him away elsewhere....

He felt Eve's eyes burrowing into the back of his head, heard the dirge in her voice, commenting, "So soon the tree turns bare!" and he wondered that she would say what she did, and what was that new note of despair? He forced himself to turn around, keeping his eyes raised to her face; noting especially the added lines on her cheeks and forehead that unrecognized what she had been only this morning, the dead fire in her eyes.

"Yet, it flourishes!" he told her, greatly surprised that she had said what she did. "Still, the leaves sing on every branch. And the fruit dances!"

Eve heard him with scorn and pity. Most of all, she took fright at that child-like awe that tinkled in his voice over such a distance that she despaired of his manhood and the joining of their separate visions ... unless Adam partook.

"Both of his eyes have the same sight and un-sight," thus, did she flatter herself over what she had gained by comparison, since biting the fruit, and the duality of vision was added to the dialogue of her inner voices: one eye for each voice.

The juices of the fruit were now streaming in her blood and flooding her senses until nothing would ever again seem as before. This new dominion was a total environment, influencing the further person with new scripts for new stages, in a drama of altered distinctions between what was right, or wrong and where the balances between flesh and spirit tottered between need without gratitude, revolt without love. That moment, Eve was as different from

Adam as the ape from both of them!

Caught up at the crest of transformation, Eve cried out with all her force: "Adam!" It was the last familiar note and the most important part of her past: she would try to hold onto it.

Adam heard the pleasure in her voice, not the pain. "Eve," he replied, different in his urgency, filling the space between them.

The serpent made it a trio. "Queen without a king!" he interjected; raising the hand that held the fruit.

"If she has bitten, so have I," Adam replied hastily, completely without guile. "Are we not one of the same flesh?"

The serpent looked at Adam with curious and friendly eyes, then laughed between his fingers. "A woman will rule Eden," he responded. "*She*, above all!" he added matter-of-factly. "After all, Eve has taken the privilege."

The serpent was now between them, leaning on the trunk of *that* tree with the utmost composure. Both Adam and Eve had the beginnings of a thought; neither one of which would reach up and capture them: in Eve was the mournful bell tolling through the dense fog, warning, No, not yet! Wait until I understand this strangeness that seizes me! In Adam, the remembered voice of God was coming through: not stern and restrictive as, at first, it had sounded, but, soft and guiding, lest he fall. But Adam's ear was not turned that way.

His eye was full on Eve, who was now taking another fruit from the tree, kicking behind her the new-fallen branch.

"She knows good. She knows evil. She has become like God!" He shouted without a voice, inside himself.

He spurned the fruit she held out to him, taking instead the one she had already bitten into, seizing it between his teeth, munching, swallowing, then, jumping up and down and pounding his chest, he cried out a fierce challenge to no one in particular. Together, they climbed the tree, and began to swing from its branches.

Part 7

POST-SCRIPTURAL

"Thus did Eve become one huge hole; all entrances and exits." Satan slammed the pages together of the huge tome he was carrying with a loud thud, and settled back with that comfortable, smug air that surely must precede a long and elaborate commentary. "What if the fruit still hung intact on that tree, did you ask?"

Jesus had not been considering this at all, but Satan was hardly fazed by such unrhetorical impediments. Indeed, he was now zooming in with strong responses to the question that had never been asked. "I curry no favor with that school of exegesis who exercise their daydreams with what-if's. Power ... not parables! Persuasion ... not pity! 'What is' is God, is scripture. The rest: followers."

Satan flung down his tome at Jesus' feet.

"There! Change a word of it!" He snorted with a great display of contempt. "Exchange words with me on Theology, debate me on morals, contradict me on Astrology. But on matters of scripture: pay attention! I defy you to find a single scroll without my mark on it! Twist and shape and form any letter into words, and words upon words; and let them face up to the sky with trails of smoke, or burn below through the sands: there! There is my own mark!"

Satan began to pace back and forth, having worked himself into a state of righteous indignation. It would be impossible for Jesus to ignore him, waving his hands in futile gestures of impatience, gnashing his teeth as if he couldn't begin to say all that rioted within him. "In my kingdom, everyone is an amateur theologian. If you could see us bent over the book, haggling over minute inflections, sifting the syllables for a grain of gold... But the clue, the key, the secret is what has not been said. The truth is between the lines."

Satan paused to study the expression on Jesus' face; begging favor for his philanthropy; pressing his point one degree further, "The commentary is an improvement over the text!"

As yet, not even a sign that he had heard, from Jesus. Then, Satan saw the muscles under Jesus' cheeks ripple, and he dug in further, "Underneath, Jesus, underneath those fading Hebrew letters that we politely call 'The History of the Peoples of Adam' is, in truth, and more to the point...."

"No, Satan ..." Jesus sounded surprisingly mild; overly patient, in fact; replying as one might to an overly enthusiastic schoolboy who has looked north and south, but not east or west, up and down, inward and outward, from near or afar in giving evidence. " ... above all commentaries is the Source. The reflection is not its own light; anymore than that which takes substance from the life of the soul is greater than its origin, except that our Lord wills it so, adding the Breath to the clay. Even thus, Satan, can you disdain the wisdom that introduced the light to thee? And then, again, His mercy that sanctions 'No!' even as it defiles that which is greatest among the greatness of Creation. Is there a place for that in thy scroll?"

Jesus could see that something had seeped under the skin of Satan ... perhaps only that the surface mildness of what Jesus was saying effectively disarmed Satan's usual riposte to any lunge; even imply-ing the existence of a vulnerability to love in the great satirist him-self. The powerful thrust of what Jesus was formulating was ignited, and burst into flame with this last summation: "After all, had He not loved thee in thy light; surely thou wouldst exceed His patience in thy darkness!"

Satan's eyes were furrowed in the flesh; growing tight within their pouches, then sharpening as they thrust upward. "How did I love Thee!" Satan called out to the emptiness above his head; and in one bewildering moment, the ripening of a long anguish showed the thorns and bristles where it and the spirit were joined. Finally it was exposed, to be seen for what it was: tactics for survival. This, then, was what Satan confronted, together with Jesus, within their separate wildernesses. Never before had the mask fallen so far down Satan's face!

It was painful to watch, yet Jesus did not take his eyes away; nor did he retreat from further intimacy, though recognizing the inher-ent perils when the remains of a conscience is driven from its last refuge, without further hiding place.

There was a further resolution. Satan lowered his head and charged forward holding a lance almost as old as time. "Don't keep blaming the serpent!" Satan hurled his challenge. "The worm was not in the fruit, the fruit is the worm! Tempt me, Jesus. One of us must, and will bite the fruit, else, why and wherefore this crossed path where we meet? Before we were was temptation! How many times a day, for what number of years and bundles of centuries must Adam go by that tree, and resist?! Into the breach, I rose to the spur!" Satan shouted.

Jesus shuddered at the exultant thrill of the cutting voice, already celebrating the inevitabilities. He saw the eye of Satan full on his flesh, reading him with frigid lust and amusement; taking pleasure in his torment, and Jesus spoke to the One who watched and knew all, whispering from where the first breath began, "Thy will be done."

Then it was that a wind rose up in the desert; one of those strange and unpredictable gusts that appear whimsically from nowhere and leave with the same suddenness. Except this one was not hot and dust-laden, choking the throat, but rather caressed the brow of Jesus, cool and softly perfumed with myrrh and frankincense, a balm of the Holy Spirit, a kiss from God.

There was that in the face of Jesus now which was beyond Satan's immediate comprehension and he gave respect to it, seeing that Jesus was in the spirit, and ready to speak.

"What hast thou brought to the work of God, Satan? Where once a garden was planted, you have grown weeds to suffocate the flowers; plaguing the fruit with thy worms. And then, while all creation laughed and took delight in that fulfillment which was the majesty of man; you conspired his fall and degeneration. Out of the cradle to the rot of flesh, enslaving the spirit to the senses, that it seek its own corruption and demise.

"How you take vengeance on what was pure in God's image: seeing the cleanliness become pestilence; not even turning aside in pity, but taking joy in their indignities; dancing to celebrate the green and brown mold that is the disease of their precious soul. You have extolled the loss of innocence; daring the temple wherein God lodged His own breath to defile it with thy own excrescencies. It is not man, it is God you attack!"

And Jesus looked at Satan with a steady eye; nailing each vice down with a hammer blow, "Pride! Covetousness! Lust! Anger! Gluttony! Envy! Sloth!"

But that which Jesus had given to shame was lost upon Satan, even eliciting new pride. He folded his hands together, haughtily awaiting more.

Jesus, sorrowed at this, continued what had to be said, "What to Adam was bequeathed was not given to the beasts. Such a gift bears its own responsibility—and you knew it, Satan! From the beginning, you had your eye on the exercise of Adam's soul. You knew that neither Adam nor Eve would choose to bring themselves below the beast. How did you bring the child to say 'no' to the Father? What did you sponsor to defeat love? How does one abuse freedom to be no longer free? Who, more than you, might have warned them of the consequences of rebellion!"

Here it was not possible for Jesus to continue before he had wept openly and relieved the heaviness of his heart. "That your eyes may be opened, this is what you told them, even as you sealed their lids that they might not take fright in death, that you may be like God: this, in the ears of the ones already like God who became now more like Satan. And the knowledge of good and evil was *you*, was Satan. And they entered the world of your distortions, your convex and concave images, and they learned what Lucifer forgot and Satan remembers. They lost sight of the one and only reality; the truth, without which, the rest are lies, the world without sin!"

Satan began to squirm as if there were a bad taste in his mouth and a burning in his bowels. Yet, he tried to maintain his repose, screwing up his face, and chewing on his tongue as if to appear indifferent.

But it was not over yet. Jesus was not to be repressed. "If you remember nothing else, Satan, remember this. *That which is from the fingers of God and bears His breath is and will be forever holy!* No matter, you lead Adam to pasture in the wallow of pigs or seek to expunge the sacred flame in a flood of indulgences. One spark is always there in the depth of the deepest dark where you cannot reach. One day that breath which would have blown out the flame will, instead, ignite the spark and burn a hole in the darkest night ..."

Jesus kneeled, and clasped his hands fervently, "I devote myself! I pray that it finds the light."

CHAPTER FOUR
DIASPORA

He could not abide,

without aversion,

the sins of pride and perversion

that take their toll

within the soul.

Part 1

FRUIT OF THE FRUIT

Searching out every corner of the then-known earth; now was heard the loneliest cry; and the cry withered the bloom, and introduced tragedy to the innermost cave of each ear that heard it, burying the sound farthest from the light. "Adam! Where are you?"

There would be a day again when another father of lesser spirit limited by the flesh, would be sifting the ashes, seeking out his lost children in the dark, among the damned and fallen, and the echo of that first anguish would rise in him that he could sense the greater-love-greater-pain of those first wild and searching words. "Eve! Where are you?"

Eve was the first to hear, hearing what she did not want to hear, putting her arms around Adam's waist and burying her face in his chest.

Adam's arms were like branches around her, but now, he was grown limp and rooted in intense silence, straining toward that ball of sound whose bass notes were crackling with distant drum rolls.

The impulse to run away was not as strong as his need, no matter how profound his dismay, to confront the sound, now approaching more rapidly, hovering over his head, bleak and threatening. He closed his pores even as his skin prickled with fear, suspecting whence it came.

"ADAM!"

The horizon closed in swiftly, imprisoning him, a fetus within its fold, not yet come to term.

"EVE!"

At last, finally relieving the impossible tension, the thunder.

Adam looked at Eve, who, it seemed, would have rejoined her separate self to the hollow of his lost rib, and her fear joined to his, bursting toward frenzy. He pushed her away from him, repudiating their common identity; and he looked to the sky, blubbering, "It

was the woman you gave to me, the one you put beside me, she was
first! She tempted me, and I did not know how to resist!" It bub-
bled, frothed, then rushed out of him in great spouts.

"EVE! What have you done?"

Without Adam to lean on, Eve came back on her heels; her head
bent over, feeling faint. Above her head, she could feel the clouds
hanging like claws. It was a grim and terrible arena, yet not without
a desperate hope: the soul might yet shine through!

What was at the end of that long wait? Why did the breath of
God suspend itself nearest her heart? Could it be shame, shame
relinquishing its last defenses, submitting to the mercy of the
Divine? Did she hear His love beneath the pain and beyond the
anger?

Terrible, terrible pendulum begging the fullness of time again!
Perhaps, a sign of true remorse? Eve! Show the way to Adam! At least
one humble word ... try, try anything! That part of innate nobility
that yields grace to love ... say with your tongue, Eve; some token
that bespeaks purity. If you will only yield the miser's portion, spell
out the word that means gratitude, forswear by inference; reject by
contrition; be naked to justice; the tiniest nod to Love; the mite of
an act that demeans the lie, asking forgiveness. Eve! Call sin by its
name: begin your plea for a new baptism, even a Queen must bend
her head in confession. But, not, not contrariness! Do not accuse
God!

When Eve ended her silence, and spoke at last; her words were
measured, parading slow and stately cadences: "The serpent! It was
Your serpent. That one behind *that* tree, the one to whom You gave
guile and a tongue...."

Now Adam bound himself to the side of Eve, and his voice was
borrowed from the serpent and the memory of an overhanging
shadow, "How does one make a choice between good and evil," he
began truculently; and Eve chimed in that they might finish the
question with one tongue and a common heritage, " if the meaning
of good and evil was not known to us!"

The challenge was hurled upwards, "You locked the secret in the
fruit."

Thence the moment, apart from all eternity, when time stood still, and the sun burned a hole in the sky as the earth stopped spinning; while the moon intruded, laughing. All the waters in all the seas: one giant muscle held back by the finger of God, foaming, straining, suspended, awaiting the COMMAND to unleash itself.

On earth, it was the time of the long-fanged breed; viperous heads, spitting poison, fouling the sweet smell of grass; writhing, tracing their slime to the roots, taking paternity from the remains of the clay: the offal, the entrails, the carrion bits of clay; wriggled and took life for themselves; crawling from the bowels of the earth.

It was no secret that the face of God was turned away from the earth; that evil grew seeds and multiplied. That great roar of passion was not from the mouths of insane lions, spouting whales, or angry hawks priming their beaks; their first tumult was gone by, it was the insects; ants, lice and maggots; bees and dragonflies; tics and mites with hooks and claws, all together, combining their passion, humming.

Then, as if on signal; unlearned, as if it had always been so; they turned, one upon the other; weaker below; stronger above the heap, tasting flesh, drinking blood.

And Adam with his wife; and Eve with her husband: together, they heard the muffled cries from the ghosts of the seeds of future centuries, reaching them in unborn voices at the dying end of a wind in the language of the rain on the leaves, and they might have heard more of the despairing sighs and groans of sorrow, if their own storms and fevers had not possessed them.

They went about the business of begetting patriarchies and matriarchies with such zest and zeal that, incredible as it may seem, it was a long while in between before they were fully conscious and aware ... they were no longer in Eden.

Part 2
RETREAT AND REVEILLE

The second week began furled in shrouds.

The earth shuddered and braced itself against the wrath of God. Shriveled to the core it was as if, by contracting its expanse, it would become less vulnerable. Meanwhile, the forces of evil multiplied more rapidly than anything else. They came out of hiding; from behind the clouds, burrowing out of holes in the earth, slithering from underwater caves; even facing the sun with assurance that the burning eyes of God were elsewhere. Could it be possible that the work of creation was merely a stage setting for a monumental orgy? Where was the fury of God?

Adam and Eve looked at one another: fear was mirrored in each other's eyes. Wee tiny voices that had been content with shadows now rose up more fiercely, squealing with pleasure and taking delight in what was become an endless night. Teeth chattering, the first man and woman became more like simians, hiding in the farthest depth of the first cave they found. The fierce winds sought out the frames of their bones, they grew hair on their skin, becoming wild at the thought of having lost the sun; simpering, whimpering; near to insanity; the memory of Eden burned temporarily out of their minds that they might survive their eviction.

The next dawn was in reveille. It would seem they had surrendered the right to open their eyes. Willingly! And, although, their hands were pressed tight against their ears, they could still hear the strident shrieks; the rise and fall wailing of the serpent; receiving his wage.

First the tongue; stretched out long and rubbery from the root of his throat; forking, falsetto with curse and shriek; lashing, writhing venom; alarm, recognizing the true cause of fear. Now, were his arms unscrewed; rocking loose in the socket; clenched fist unclenched; unwilled; unbelonging; all writhing together in convulsive agony. The torso still strained upward; given support by fury beyond pain, stabbing roots of feet to the trunk; agony, to replace the lost branches. But not for long!

The serpent fell with a scream that pounded the top of mountains; compressing hate, also fear in its living, elongated remains. Hard and angry scales forming, its skin waving in half-circles, the remains of muscle in motion; moving, desperately moving over the sharp stones on raw flesh; bruising the gaps where limbs had been.

For the first and last time, one tear froze its pearl and fell, glazing fire into ice; green slits of eyes, unblinking.

And, as it drew away, unready to die; its forked tongue waved side to side, ready to strike, pierce with venom, anyone who remembered its pride. Thus, sliding, slipping, probing the hole in the earth most in depth; the serpent escaped the light.

The long night in the cradle was over. The cradle was upturned, but was this a nursery in which they found themselves? The suckle was not there anymore, and their lips swallowed the treacherous air. It was an interrupted middle of the night with nothing to soothe their fears. From no one, not their own Father, did they dare beg for warmth, for food and water. They wept, apart from each other.

It was no more than the surface of innocence they had lost in Eden. The time had been too short. They were still children; lost to meaning, and all that followed on the knowledge of good and evil was remote from subtle distinctions, a long, long way from maturity. Whatever the maze of choices before Adam, before Eve; nothing could take the place of the large hand of God over their heads! Children, knowing love, never ask, why the milk? Why the care? Why the comfort? The bite of the fruit asked why!

If they had brought nothing else away with them from Eden; no matter how distant the wonder, how far away the memory now seemed; it was one of uninterrupted openness, the wide-open welcoming arms of space. Now, they dwelt in a cave.

The daily struggle to maintain life was of the same natural order as the inhalation of breath; both of which were no longer recognized as gifts from their Creator. They gratified survival with the most primitive ceremonies; learning most crudely that they could no longer reach overhead leisurely and the branches would supply their needs. The fruit was falling foul on the ground in Eden.

At first, they spent long hours groping above their heads mechanically, until their arms grew heavy and fell to their sides futilely. It was the anguish in their stomachs that finally brought them to their knees. And they explored their cave with fingers that had become sensitized. In this way they came upon an answer to hunger in the form of green, gray and yellow patches of mossy lichen. This they brought to their mouth, finding it palatable. Sometimes, black ants and white worms would crawl on their fingers out of the moss; and sometimes they ate what was in their hands, becoming less and less fastidious as their needs increased.

There were those endless nights in the cave; sitting back to back, chewing meditatively, grunting and groaning primevally; more akin to two-legged beasts, and far from the original clay.

Once, sitting hunched against an intruding wind, their keen ears detected a new sound; a rustling movement and quick panting of breath. They gripped each other's arms in terror at first; until they saw that it was a young rabbit, wet with rain, who had wandered inside the cave for refuge.

The rabbit regarded them tensely, then relaxed, seeing that they shared the same misery. Eve held out a handful of moss and, hesitantly at first, then beyond caution, the rabbit eased into their circle, nibbling out of her fingers.

Adam looked at Eve meaningfully, a rough smile curling his lips. He touched the back of the rabbit, feeling the skin quiver under his fingers. Eve was shuddering, looking at the head of the rabbit as it nibbled; now raising its head with a sudden premonition, regarding her with some question in its open, brown eyes. The rabbit hunched its back ... Adam squeezed both hands around the rabbit's throat.

Now that there was blood on their lips, they had gone beyond the cradle. Good and evil merged ... becoming survival. The stir inside themselves, uneasy at first, reinforced their restlessness. For the first time, Adam stood fully upright. Eve stretched. Why? They never understood. But it was time ... time to leave the cave.

A muted sun had entered the sky. Carefully, Adam led his wife outside. The blindness was in both their eyes and it was good that the light of day was diffused. Even so, it was not yet a kindness. Then the blur became shadow; finally taking on color through the haze. They saw the green grass and the blue tops of the curving hills first; filtered and drab as it would seem against the least corner of Eden, to their eyes, the open and fresh beauty they beheld was beyond comparison—hunger redeemed.

Now was the heaviness gone from their hearts; and they could take some steps away from the dark hole where they had thought to conceal themselves from the fate of the serpent. They listened, tasting the sound of birds and crickets. An elephant saw them emerging and trumpeted. Eve clutched at Adam who was turning pale, ready to swing around on one foot and return to the cave. But, no! It was not Him!

The elephant's signal would seem to be prearranged, for suddenly, the quiet and lifeless landscape woke up to a thunderous chorus of animal voices and between the tiny mouse and the neck of the giraffe was a variety of species numbering all but one: the serpent was conspicuously absent, a loss of presence of which they were both aware as it sounded a warning knell that dampened their rising spirits.

Adam looked at Eve, feeling uneasy, wanting to remind her of primary fault if only to relieve his own burden. He bit on his tongue and remained silent, tasting the blood in his mouth, knowing that if he spoke again, he would do with her as he had done with the rabbit ... and then he would be alone. The threat left his eyes and he drew Eve closer to his side, seeking her warmth, drawing comfort from her touch.

It was more difficult for Eve. She had seen the accusation in Adam's eyes; but she had not even thought to defend her complicity. It would seem that the punishment of God was as natural to her as her sequence with the serpent. What she could not escape from was that torture chamber always within her where the serpent's screams became confused with Adam's rejection of her before their Accuser, making her accept her own unworthiness. In her own image, she was less than the serpent. What's more, it didn't matter!

Should it have been necessary to defend herself against Adam; she might have destroyed the future of their love with one flick of her tongue: "Are we not one flesh?" That far, and that destructively, she would not go.

On the surface, however, it was Adam who was more voluble, agonizing: "We have sinned against God!" Eve looked at him gratefully.

Now Adam proved that he had gone beyond childhood; gone beyond the bareness of pain and the cry in the night without recourse. His anger found a voice: "Are we not punished enough!"

Eve gasped. She drew away from Adam, regarding him with horror, not wanting to share what must be a fiery bolt from Heaven, consuming him, but the sky retained its gentle look; the earth remained closed.

One moan followed another on Adam's lips, growing in crescendo, mixing pain and anger, becoming hysteria. His head snapped back and he pounded his fists together, bellowing at the sky: "Was it for *this* we were created?"

The silence seemed to press its lips together; imitating Eve, who was covering her mouth.

Rage and violence came to madness and the shudder ceased vibrating in Adam's body. All at once, he began to run, making wild circles of his arms, threshing the air. When he reached the side of the mountain, his speed increased; and he leapt, flinging himself against the rock, beating at it with his fists.

Eve caught up to him at last, not touching him, but watching in profound confusion, unwilling to understand. Adam turned to her, dazed, scarcely conscious, open-mouthed, he showed her his hands, raising them before her face so that she could see the dripping blood, so that he could prove by the red pulp of his flesh, how much he had suffered.

Eve was unable to meet her feelings. "Adam," she whispered, repeating his name over and over again senselessly, until she understood. Adam was showing her; but, really he was giving testimony to God, punishing himself so that God would stop punishing, even threatening God with his own death.

It was the ninth hour of the ninth day. Adam was alone in the world. Eloi, Eloi ... why this night above all other nights! The darkness wept ... *lama sabachtani?*

Part 3
PILGRIMAGE

Taking leave of the cave, and joining this new and other world had taken its toll on their energies; and, like children only recently able to walk, curiosity was its own purpose. In those several dawns since the life of the cave, they might not have gone very far afield had it not been for the need to forage for food and shelter at night. Berries and fruits were certainly not within reach and they were not fast or strong enough to manage any but the smaller beasts; or sniff out the occasional fowl. At best, their hunting tactics were hit or miss, not at all dependable.

There they were, just emerging from the forest, trampling through a wide plain of foot-high grasses, Eve behind Adam, mostly silent and apart from each other, grunting signals to one another mainly about bodily needs and functions. Generally, directions didn't matter; and it was not long before they began to recognize the lay of the land: where they might expect to find a running brook, something for their gnawing bowels, and a shelter where they could take refuge.

It was in the darkness, knowing that night was at hand, that they sought and found one another. It was as if the spread over their heads of a tight sky in which the sun disappeared brought forth that profound and mysterious bondage within the darkness of each self. Thus, one might commune with the approach of night. Thus, both could share one body, united as in the beginning.

Something more, however, had been transfigured in Eve. In the daylight, she dragged her feet and paused more frequently; and then there was that sweet and pensive smile threatening always to become laughter. Even Adam, in his own crude way, began to recognize a source of warmth and radiance within his companion to which he responded with fumbling tenderness.

What was being held aloft was to become a beacon for future generations. For Adam, it was translated as that sense of peace and satisfaction, the highlight of his day that reminded him at last of Eden.

At first, it had warmed his insides, just the recollection that Eden existed; then came despair at the memory of what they had lost and the drabness and meager light in which they found themselves; after which, the source of his fear returned, and he bethought himself of a cave again where he might hide from God...

Eve saw the veil come over his eyes; and, looking through it, she grew wise to the meaning of the heavy clouds hanging over her man's soul. Her own guilt did not fill a space in her heart that moment; having been first was of no consequence; not anymore. Although she found herself becoming more dependent on Adam for his strength and inventiveness, at the same time, she saw plainly that she exceeded him in grasp and depth of feeling; sensitive even to what had not been said nor yet experienced. She became mother as well as wife to her man.

She reached out her hand toward his in the semi-darkness. "No, Adam. We shall not return to the cave."

Adam glanced at her sideward, happy at the sight of her, purring softly; yet not up to confessing his joy. Had he not once been king?!

Eve embraced her new girth; then, folding her hands in her lap, she lapsed off, dreaming, her half-closed eyes resting eastward over the raw bones of the great mountains where Eden had been. It would seem that the crimson rays in the sky pulsed from an invisible core through that rent in the sky, proving that God had not lost sight of them.

"It is the dawn," Adam said it like a prayer, hushed and solemn. His face took on softness. The red glow of light delineated the wonder that rose in his throat, past the bony gate of flesh that had tried without success to block the forbidden fruit.

They rose to their feet; their bodies touching; watching the light entering their world; not yet daring complete joy. The shimmering edge of the sun was nearly on the horizon, and the air was fresh in their nostrils. Adam called to mind how it was in Eden when the Holy Spirit was close by; and his eyes filled with tears, if only because this dawn promised the renewal of love; that He had not abandoned them.

Eve saw the tears of Adam's cheeks and she brought his head down to rest on her bosom, and they wept together, holding tight to one another.

Now, the edges of the silver light were touched by orange fires; the last lingering stars backed off with a promise of return; the clouds curtseyed; and the unmuted sun burst forth with heralds of song and dance and unrepressed laughter.

Adam's whole spirit leaped up in greeting; throwing off the flesh momentarily. "Tonight!" he shouted. "Tonight, we rest in Eden!"

Was it also a law of nature before the Fall that the way downward contributes to momentum; or is it so that obstacles are neither there in the loom of the perfect way; or below conceit when the spirit flourishes in its own sphere and identities?

The way backward was also the forward way, as if Adam and Eve would have to traverse all the length of the earth, to return whence they came. Return, not retreat!

Should there be moments when the quake of memory would find them shivering before that tree once more, God, searching them out, they were counter-balanced by the new found courage emerging from their elation over the discovery of that extra wing called *Hope*. Else, how account for the drive that forded the rivers between waterfalls, spread open the vines that choked their road, kept them moving in the night past the caves that could again hide them from the red eye of their own fears. At last they found themselves at the big toe of some great mountains. Here, they paused, looking at one another, expecting to be recharged for the last impetus and not finding it in the other's wavering glances, they rested.

The last barrier was a mountain, not the one before their eyes whose immensity, of itself, constituted a prodigious challenge. The true challenge was within themselves.

They looked up where the mountain dared to touch the sky and they were frightened, they were frightened and naked beyond the visible flesh. Even as they sought the inner strength to humble the mountain, the bare insolence of the act compelled both of them to confront their defiance.

If it was Eve who first began to recognize the pain of God, it was

Adam who was forced to acknowledge that He had been merciful. And they wrung their hands, and wept, pitying their own misfortune. Eve thought bitterly of leaving; not even attempting the mountain. If it were not for the new heartbeat and pulse within her body; no doubt, she would have given way to her wretchedness, nor would Adam have given her pause. He found hiding within the furthest shadows, leaning away not to be seen, the direst recognition of all; the one that went beyond shame or guilt and would not be accounted for by forgiveness and one more chance ... the depth of Adam's forlorn agony, putting aside remorse, was this ... sin would happen all over again!

To her horror, Eve saw how far Adam had gone, even to the point of no return, and she dug her nails into his flesh, pulling him close to her with all her strength. "It did not come from us!" She stabbed the words into him, over and over again. "The serpent! The serpent!" she breathed into his ear; and when he was full with what she had said, he fell against her, she against him, and they slept, saving themselves for the next morning.

The polished and sculptured sides of the mountain thrusting an open palm before them to make their further way impossible, of itself, it was a true monument to the winds and upper storms that had chopped and planed its sides, a mighty penitent, shriven of rebellion; snow-haired, looking down with contempt on whosoever would dare an ascent.

Yet, how strange!

If it had been an upward jaunt straight to the peak, in their present state of mind, neither Adam nor Eve would have begun. To do so would have invited an immediate confrontation at the gates of Eden and after last night's glimmer; their eyes turned inward toward foreboding landscapes; they were scarcely prepared to meet their Creator. On the other hand, the very impossibility of the barrier; that it dwarfed them so; not asking, but ordering them to concede; granting no respect to spirit, or will, or inventiveness. That they took even one step up the sheer rise spoke of the breath of God within them! The soul was no burden to those spindly legs on their first climb, in fact, it seemed always to precede them in their progress.

They had reached the lower haunch of the great mountain. So far it had been a surge and swell of song carried along by its own exhilaration. Wisely, they had kept their eyes averted from any full glance upward, postponing totality until, at least spatially, it could be kept in distant focus. As yet, they did not know, or even dream, that there was much more than sheer physical bulk to contend with, nor did the touch of its tentacles define it. Not until their evolution upward had gone beyond the last trees, and the bushes had become more scattered.

There was a new shriek in the winds above their heads; and the air was alive with voices, a gibbering menage of disembodied sounds that cut-off below the point of recognition, or reversed themselves backwards from crescendo. Adam recalled that same cacophony the first days away from Eden. At the time, in the fever of speed and fear of God's pursuit, it had gone over the threshold of hearing in the deadening course of frenzy. Now, he understood that evil was giving birth.

There was a new force in the world; an incomprehensible one that, even in Eden, could say 'no'. What else could it be that became choleric and wild in view of their affirmation? Each time they took a step, there would be a howl to turn their glances downward in dizzying perspective; distracting them, causing a tumble that was almost fatal. Their feet became heavy as if the weight of demons were pulling down on them, leading them into despair. Where they had been confident before, now they were obsessed by the fear of falling. What had been courage before, now was foolhardiness. If anything kept them going, shouting encouragement to one another, it was that the way down seemed just as perilous.

IT CANNOT BE DONE!

Was that the voice of the serpent? The same voice that promised they would become like God?

They looked up with tortured eyes and saw the snow and ice yet to come and their bodies sagged. Eve groaned out loud, unwilling to concede, driven by a life force she could not put into words. Even as they kept slipping back, she strained forward a little at a time, grim and determined.

Adam fought his way beside her, inspired by her struggle, unwilling to be left behind. Thus, they reached the next ledge, and were able to draw breath for awhile, albeit, painfully.

This time, Adam took the initiative; crawling, sliding, agonizing over each gain, with Eve not far behind. More than half the distance was behind them; and just as hope began to thaw in their hearts, they looked up and saw great boulders of stone loosened and rolling down with thunderous sounds between and beside them. They screamed to each other, using up their reserve of strength; managing at least to dodge the treacherous missiles. Exhausted, they held on to one another, just to remain standing, and not to collapse.

The sky darkened and the snow began to fall. The tears were freezing on Eve's cheeks. When she looked up in the last throes of anguish, she beheld a deep-rooted bush of red berries appearing like a wound on the mound of snow. She pointed it out to Adam, shouting hysterically, "There! There!"

The red gashes were everywhere, going up ... up ... they tried the first branch. It gave them support; even the sweet bitterness of its fruit.

Now, they climbed easily; each bush supporting them, pulling them higher, higher, higher—in sight of the upper plateau!

It was a delirium: their bodies pressed against the cold stone, hand over hand, mumbling and crying to one another their first real words in the alphabet of faith.

It would seem they had prevailed! They had arrived at the false peak; the one which, when seen from below, had appeared flat against the sky. Not yet. This was the uppermost ledge, however; with its own plain of snow; and some evergreens bent backwards in contour with the north winds. For all its grim stolidity; the sight of the final incline ahead, rising with comparative ease, was an occasion to throw off their controlled tensions, celebrating by rolling in the snow, and shouting their joy. Just *this*: then, Eden!

They chased after one another over the intervening distance, feeling light and airy; brimming over with pride; wanting to shout, then shouting, that He might look down, and take notice.

Despite the approach of night and darkness, they fully anticipated a quick and easy ascent, resting finally there where the winds did not blow through their bones, and peace is forever of the moment.

Adam was faster; first to arrive at the incline; bursting for want of breath. He touched the sides for support; then, shrieking without wind in his lungs, he collapsed in a heap at Eve's feet. She bent over his body, growing alarmed at the insane glare in his eyes, following the direction of his arm to where he was pointing; fearful, seeking with her fingers as the twilight deepened. She didn't scream. She didn't panic. Her face hardened with the shock of it; as if doubt had always been there. The fire had gone dead in her eyes.

Ice! Frozen, burning ice! The last upthrust was impossible: layer upon layer of granite snow polished to a mirror-gleam by abrasive wind, itself sliding off the smooth and slippery sides.

Adam leaped up with a sudden desperate impulse; trying to dig his nails in for even the slightest grip: not a scratch on the surface. Next he lifted Eve to his shoulders that she might feel out the higher surface for anchorage and a human chain. The ice burned into them, endurable only if ... but no!

Thus, the night came upon them; and, with it, the fierceness of another wind-driven snow. They joined their torments, body to body, teeth chattering over the dirge of their cruel fate.

That they survived the night had less to do with hope than hardiness. That they had come so far, so high, so uselessly, was a bitterness they could not cope with. There was no reason to expect another meaning to emerge from this any more than the serpent could expect to walk upright again. The gray light, when it came, did not improve matters, in fact, it made visible the cumulus of a new storm.

Eve, holding her middle, walked web-footed over to the side where she could look down, and brood over the descent. At least, compared to Adam, this was not total negation. His head lolled to one side; and his eyes expressed that blank indifference where sight has let go of content. Neither one knew that the sun was there behind the clouds, and still rising...

The first sign was a drop of fallen ice. He heard it, without hearing it: another snowfall. Next, a piece of ice fell on his head, and he stirred ever so slightly, not bothering to wipe his cheeks; leaning back, rolling his eyes slowly upward. He sniffled. He began to cry softly...

Eve looked at him; and saw what he was pointing at. "The ice is crying," she commented painfully through cracked lips. "Over us?"

She saw that Adam was stirring; coming up on his elbows, an incredulous look on his face, shouting at her, "For us!" Life was in his eyes again. "Yes, for us!"

The blood raced through his veins, and he leaped up to embrace Eve, pulling her up with great urgency. He put all his weight to it, shinnied up; signaling Eve to follow. "Hurry!"

Up they went, racing against the warming sun, supported by the frozen tears whose short life was to be their salvation.

They dug in with their fingers without reverence; pulling themselves astride the upper earth. Pride they had left behind at the foot of the last incline. All that remained was the sense of having gone and arrived—beyond themselves.

They could feel the sun about to rise though it was out of sight, warming their purpled flesh and sending the blood coursing through their dilating veins like a young stream following winter with the anniversary of spring. Now they were upright, panting with exhaustion, trying to see ahead through the morning mist.

One hesitant step forward; and they paused on the balls of their feet, unsure of the next moment; dwarfed by the very immensity of their expectations.

All the while distant rays kept silently drilling through the mist; filtering silver light inside the bank of moisture; softening its ponderousness. Red, orange, and green sparklets shimmered like stars in the gossamer fabric; and the veil, having been pierced, lifted like a mask. Before their eyes were the fields of forever, all of Creation was there! Just as God had seen it in the clay.

It was a spectacular congregation; more than the eye could contain at once, even unto the Mite on the shoulder of Behemoth, and the Midge on the fin of Leviathan. The surprise was that the earth could hold it all without rocking and gapping. Amid all this, how awesome were the silences and the holes in space filled with eyes, all as one, turned toward Adam and Eve, all waiting as if they had been expected, as if they had entered a temple to pray, and found themselves worshipped. What profound hope had followed their upward course!

With all of nature in attendance, joined to their common fate, suddenly, it was too much to bear. Adam could not contain it and he joined hands with Eve that she might command their pain and pleasure, open the court for justice.

Nor did Eve know what was demanded of her. She looked upon the living sea and was melted down by the myriad of eyes reflecting her own ache and longing and she yearned for the time again when once more they could rest beside the sleeping lion in Eden.

Not knowing what else to do, they came forward as encouraged by the larger beasts who opened a path for them; restraining the heave of their breathing as Adam and Eve went by, not to give offence, or stir up fears. Even so, an occasional head would waggle out of the mass, fix on them with liquid eyes, making petition with murmured sounds.

The path between the beasts wended through the moonlit night from one dawn to the other ... and yet there were forms of life waiting to be seen. Merely to have conceived all this! Adam bent his head.

At last they came to an immense clearing and even if there had been no sight of angels, they would have known that here was where God had been when He came on earth. There was no garden, no incense, no music, no coronas of light. Just the certain sense of the holy and sacred transcending the need for proof and evidence. There was no line or boundary; but at its edge, no animals dared go beyond.

Each in turn, the lion and the dove; the eagle and the ant; the wolf and the lamb ... spoke the prayer for all the others: "Father, Mother, on earth; in whose hands were given our destinies. Lean thy head toward us, that we may know thy grace as it was before, and will be forever in Paradise. We pray that we may see Eve and Adam baptized; unspotted, redeemed, without sin ... for you are Saints in our midst. Lead us; plead for us; bleed our thirst; be one tongue for all our words; teach us peace, that we may be blessed by He who made thee."

In solemn procession, they walked down the aisle between the pews of animals, mother and father of all creation, growing smaller as if seen from behind as they neared the boundary, becoming, by the time they reached the breach … as children, hands linked in desperate unity, faces turned up, certain of mercy.

Now, they stood at the line, but here was a flashing brightness, making it impossible to see. Long and silver, sharp and bright, swinging back and forth from an invisible fulcrum. The vaguest outline of an angel. The incomprehensible shape of a sword, unknown before but obvious in its implications.

Adam moved impatiently to push all this aside, searching for the face of God who must surely have come, if only to rebuke. One step forward, the sword swings closer, another step: it bites!

Crying, his hand in his mouth, the metallic taste of …blood?! Shoulders hunched up to protect, body stumbling backward, still, the face of Adam turns up again in disbelief, still the eyes strain forward, unwilling to let go of hope.

Behind, a restless stir starts up among the beasts. The ones in the back shove forward, trying to see. A low growl, more like a wail of defeat, pushing out from throats that had been constricted too long in suspense. Eve raises a hand, calling for silence. Within, the kick of new life is peremptory, as if all the future generations call as well for justice. She faces the outline of the angel, not expecting, not anymore, to have audience with God.

"You! Don't I know you?" the outline trembles, the light of a candle, flickering. "Did we not play in the spray of a waterfall, singing praises as every drop flashed in the light that was the sun, that was Love?" Her chin trembles as the memory overtakes her, reminding her of all that was, and is now lost. For the moment, the sword has faltered in its swing. "I am Eve! Could it be that you don't recognize us," the possibility takes hold, begetting further courage, "This is Adam, you taught him the names of the stars…" she stops, wondering: her outstretched arms are wet with the tears of an angel.

Hope, Faith, Courage, Love. Four footsteps forward into the path of the sword. She holds her breath, half-waiting for the sting and then the redness, half-certain it cannot come. Soft...so soft, so warm and delicate and rare: the embrace of the angel as she is thrust backward—entrance barred! The shape of the angel has taken on substance in despair: for a moment, a grief-ravaged face, in torment, then a final statement: the angel has turned its back.

The storm, as if held back against its will in a gray cage of threatening clouds, escapes now in full force, pounding sideways into the faces of the waiting multitude like sharp knives: go back! Go Back! No Entrance!

Even as they hunch down together in defeat; even as the animals let loose in a frenzy of disappointment and uncomprehending rage, losing their ability to speak in one tongue; even as they turn toward the horror of the long way back down the mountain...one last time...Adam turns back, his body a question mark against the dark backdrop of the chaos erupting behind him, his arms held upward like a baby.

Part 4

THE SECOND TEMPTATION

Satan had begun to suspect that this soul in the desert was more than a mere rabbi with a mission. Yet, he held back guardedly. Who would know better, beginning with the right hand of God, how complex were the hierarchies in Heaven?

If Jesus were the Messiah, the time of bugles and trumpets and the massing of forces was at its terrible beginning. Satan trembled in spirit at the very thought. How unlikely, though! Satan turned a jaundiced eye toward Jesus; this scrawny baggage of flesh that had begun to persecute him; and, despite the inner fires he saw burning, he was not impressed. At best, a saint! One of those rare and unwelcome contradictions to Adam about whom legends spring and myths develop.

That confluence of stars, the nightmares of that wretched king, the transformation of Mary, his mother, *there* was a point! But is there a mother among the Hebrews who does not hold her firstborn son to her bosom, dreaming the song of the Messiah, the lullaby that puts the mother to sleep?

Satan continued sifting. Virginal birth, bah! Would the son of David equate sex with sin? Laugh, Solomon, laugh!

Yes, there was a hint of something or another, the child entering the synagogue, but then, is there a young man in Israel, being confirmed to his faith, who has not felt in the heat of his blood: This day, I raise my sword within the tent of Abraham!

Back and forth, pro and con, hot and cold; Satan confronted the fact that here was more than just another Jew grasping at Adam's burden. More to the point: what seed was this that was planted in the hushed darkness, now showing only the head of a carpenter's son? On whom had that burst of light fallen? And the words! Beyond all else said of man by God, My Beloved Son.

As for that self-humbled and crumpled figure of prayer lying in the sand before him; Satan was too wise to move from incredulity to its extreme contrast, which becomes superstition. Instead, he determined to forego the initiative; drawing Jesus out of his reserve, outside his depth right up to that last vulnerable edge where, at the sight of power, even the mightiest topple ... witness Lucifer!

Meanwhile, the whole clan and paternity of Satan's brood invisibly joined the landscape, recognizing that something more than the capture of one more soul was in question here. Even the gloat in Satan's voice; the delicious substance of pleasure carried to the far end of delirium, betrayed a special something. Who are you, Jesus, that you should inherit the whole sheaf of Satan's porcupine barbs?

"Jesus, son of Joseph, son of Heli, son of Matthat, Son of Levi..." Satan began his litany, shaking back and forth, beating his breast at every name; closing his eyes and adopting a cantorial sing-song that echoed the original voices of the long-gone dead.

It was another of Satan's unannounced spectacles to which Jesus gave small witness, having become inured to the force of Satan's wit. This one, however, was more than just annoying; indeed, separate voices were joining; each, a recognizable identity. On being introduced, they joined in with the crowd, beating their names on his eardrum.

The crowd was becoming a mob, "... son of Melchi, son of Jannai, son of Joseph, son of Mattathias, son of Amos, son of Nahum, son of Esli, son of Naggai, son of Maath, son of Mattathias, son of Semein, son of Josech, son of Joda, son of Joanan, son of Rhesa, son of Zerubbabel, son of Shealtiel, son of Neri, son of Melchi, son of Addi, son of Cosam, son of Elmadam, son of Er, son of Joshua, son of Eliezer, son of Jorim, son of Matthat, son of Levi ..."

Here, Satan paused, not because he was running out of names or voices, but because he could not resist a speculative glance toward Jesus to see if the chant had served its intended hypnotic effect. Unmistakably, Jesus was within himself, thus, Satan resumed, "son of Symeon, son of Judah, son of Joseph, son of Jonam, son of Eliakim, son of Melea, son of Menna, son of Mattatha, son of Nathan, son of David ... HERE IT IS! Son of David! Then you can be! You are?"

Satan tasted it on his lips. "Jesus the Messiah? Son of Man? Son of God! No, it doesn't scan," Satan interjected, turning aside and spitting. "The carpenter's boy sounds more like truth."

Having said this, Satan saw that he had lost the thread of his web, so he took up his first stance, "Son of Jesse, son of Obed, son of Boaz, son of Salan, son of Nahshon, son of Amminadab, son of Admin, son of Arni, son of Hezron, son of Perez, son of Judah, son of Jacob, son of Isaac, son of Abraham, son of Terah, son of Nahor, son of Serug, son of Reu, son of Peleg, son of Eber, son of Shelah, son of Cainan, son of Arphaxad, son of Shem, son of Noah.... Now, there was a carpenter for you!"

In passing, Jesus took note of that flaw in Satan which permitted nothing to go by without commentary; that naked pride, always clothed in opinion. At the same moment, Satan saw and raged at what Jesus had been during this long recital. That constant movement of Jesus' lips that Satan had loosely construed as the babble preceding a state of trance was far beyond that. Actually, whenever a name fell off of Satan's lips, Jesus had been picking it up like a hurt bird, praying it back to life, returning it back to the sky in flight once more.

Satan was choleric, turning yellow, green, purple and blue. "Son of ...! Son of ...! Son of ...!" he shrieked. "What does it matter? Always! Always! It ends and begins with Adam. Doesn't it, Jesus? A genealogy of puff and wind, a charade of bastardy! The combined dust of your whole ancestry would scarcely form a small boulder. Tell me, Jesus: which speck, which mite, which grain of a grain still resembles the original clay? An interesting question, you'll concede? Here's another one. You've seen what happens to yesterday's footprint in the sand when the winds blow? Still you persist in blowing against the wind; building empires in the sand ... expendable, isn't it? To what dust does the dust do honor? If you must contend, challenge me with something more than catafalques of moving sand and the fading riches of a sunrise. I've had enough of dross and pretension. But thou! The beloved Son of God! Be more of thyself, if you would make less of me!"

At the feel of Satan's hand on his shoulder, Jesus looked up sharply; but he did not resist. They rose off the ground, levitating straight upward.

It was apparent that Satan had not planned or even considered the sheer absurdity in which they were now involved. Satan was smiling now, a sly, feline look with a slightly embarrassed edge, seeming to give temperance to the extreme frustration that had precipitated this tenuous course. Was it not Satan himself who had once said 'Capture a goat with cheese; a fool with astrology; and only half a soul with the exotic.'

Had there been any sky-watchers in Jerusalem that morning, they might have seen some low-hanging wisps of clouds being blown at great speed in the direction of the Temple. No more. Even when Satan with Jesus were easing down on the highest parapet no one looked up or noticed anything strange or unusual , except certain Jews at their morning devotions who felt a sudden freeze, as if chill winds had found cracks in the beams.

Both Satan and Jesus were looking down from a great height at the square below with all the scurry of preparations for a new day and the bustle of the marketplace, carts and stands. Satan's eyes were on Jesus, seeing that he was unconcerned about his own safety, that if he had any fears, they were offset by an unflinching confidence in God's watchfulness.

Satan pointed a scornful finger at the crowds below. "There they go, on tiny feet, your adopted congregation. Look at them in their crooked dance, waving their arms and swarming over every glint of gold. What a clatter of tongues! That clutter of appendages! If they looked up and saw you here, they'd strain their necks and point you out to their children, waiting open-mouthed ... waiting to see you fall!"

Satan formed a trumpet with his hands and bellowed to the crowd below: "Here he is! The Fool of Your Faith! Your mountebank!"

Obviously, he did not expect to be heard. "More to the point is not that they look up at *you*, but that *you* look down on *them*! You may forget this perspective. You will not always be able to hide in the temple, keeping your eyes only on the tabernacle. There comes a time when the small waves touch your garments; when your white robe must become unclean in their dust; when the greedy eyes find your spirit and lust for your flesh. Can't you see how they hunger to complete themselves!"

Satan's laugh was short and ugly. "I mean their bellies! The guts! Farting out His breath!"

Jesus drew away from Satan who had been nudging him all the while, behaving as if they shared some special understanding. At the same time, in becoming aware of Satan's repugnance toward the human scene below, Jesus saw through the disguise to that part of Satan's torment that was under the torn wings of Lucifer ... there it was, painfully contrasted; the ghost of purity lost with the demon that must desecrate whatever rises toward the holy. But the leisure to ponder this was gone. Satan was upon him, pushing hard to the farthest edge of the parapet; goading him with these words, "Satisfy me that you are above the marketplace, neither pretender nor false prophet! Show me that you are more, not less, than the ones that bring the marketplace into the temple to ply their trade in the spirit. If you'll put aside all your masks, I'll forego the tokens, the amulets, the incantations and signs in the smoke. We'll forego anonymity to that proof of survival whose only test is true faith. If you, Jesus, are the Son of God, the one and only Messiah; throw yourself down from this parapet, even for the sake of scripture which says *He will put you in His Angels charge, and they will support you in their hands in case you hurt your foot against a stone.* Go!"

There it was ... Satan saw that pinched face turn slowly and without a sign of fear, confronting him. He saw the distant fire in those tired eyes and recognized an impenetrable calm by such small evidence as the fact that the right hand of Jesus, the one that rested on the edge of the stone, supporting him against a fall, was not white with a tight grip; but loose and sure. It was no surprise to hear Jesus reply to his challenge, "You must not put the Lord your God to the test."

Satan pondered further and more soberly into the remaining forty days; recognizing that the game was more than questioning the number of sands in the desert. Jesus had reduced the alternatives.

And they found themselves spinning in a mist, whirling at great speed, and reversing their route so rapidly that the last words of Jesus still hovered between them when they were back from whence they had begun.

Part 5
AN INTERMINABLE INTERMISSION

The thirtieth day in the desert was preceded by a little by-play hardly worth recalling, except as an amusement without meaning, if such is possible. In fact, this time Satan set the stage by appearing twice at the same time!

They stood before Jesus (both Satans nodding at once) in a mirror display of synchronism, incredible in separate identities, if such they were.

One of the Satans bowed to the waist with a grandiloquent flourish, announcing the theme: "The latest fashion in fission!"

Meanwhile, the other one was bending forward, keeping his knees tight-pressed together, covering the side of his mouth as if he meant to whisper a confidence without the other knowing, managing only to titter between his fingers at the thought.

Satan, the first one, opened a folding table that materialized from under his cloak, then, with all the hoopla of a magic show: a snap of his fingers and a black box appeared in the center of the table, looking ominous.

It might have seemed crudely obvious in another context; especially the flim-flammery of both Satans staring at the black box, keeping a respectful distance to give weight to its portent. But that was *Satan* on the stage, whose every frivolity is earth-bound with intention.

Now was the supreme climax; the opening of the box! Even here, unresisted, a wretched, drawn-out bit of showmanship. One Satan must hold up the velvet-lined box for inspection to show that it was empty while the other tapped the bottom to prove that it was solid. The box was put down. Alright-a-rap-on-the-side-of-the-table-and-out-will-come-a-white-rabbit-perhaps-even-the-one-Adam-had-eaten-in-the-cave.

No. Satan took out a black chess piece. "Black King!" he announced. The chess piece was wriggling between his fingers. Now the other one took out his piece, raising the living miniature above his head. "White Queen!" he shouted triumphantly, "Second born! Prime rib!"

When all the opposing pieces had taken up proper residence on the board; one of the Satans issued his first command: "White pawn move to the Queen's fourth square!" And the pawn moved itself.

"Black pawn move to the King's fourth square!" the order came from the other Satan. "Pawn takes pawn!" A shout of triumph, then the pawn belonging to the queen drew a blade from its scabbard and sliced away at the king's pawn until nothing remained to obstruct possession of the square previously occupied. The limbs of the king's pawn were flung back inside the black box, indifferently.

"Checkmate!" The voice thrilled with excitement; shocking all the white pieces into a bewilderment of confused despair. They kept turning around in their squares, moaning "Where? How?"

Meanwhile, the black Queen strode forcibly up to the white King and drew a sword, slicing the crown to toe, with one blow.

Finally, the Satan who had been playing the white side came out of shock and astonishment, sufficient to protest, "So soon! Impossible!"

"That's the game!" replied his black counterpart.

"You mean that all the elaboration, the wisdom and meditation; the rules and roles..."

"Yes, yes," the other insisted.

"You mean that all the labor, creating a game with flavor, carving the pieces, giving them leases; each one on a perfect black or white square ... all that..."

"Yes, yes," this time, getting bored and more indifferent.

"...and then, with one stroke, right at the start; you've become Lord of that whole flat and polished board?!"

"Yes, yes! In accord with regulation, setting apart further speculation: you're all fools when I make the rules!"

"With all this creation, what have I lost? What change can I make in the clay, if, once more, I hope to play?"

"Simple. Simple. Hide your horns, put fig leaves on your pawns; hate the bait; and bait your fate. Open the gate of Eden, still remaining a heathen. Looking above, pretending to love, put out the bait ...Checkmate!"

Of course, Jesus recognized the unholiness in making trivia of the act of Creation. Yet, following the charade and not responding immediately to that which offended him, indeed, taking that risk against the revulsion of his spirit, enabled him in this instance, to gain an important glimpse into the workings of Satan's mind.

To the degenerate eye, the knowledge of good and evil becomes the choice between good and evil, as if two thrones were in question! As for 'sin,' it was merely the free negation of the proud spirit; the choice of will escaping from conformity. Finally, it was more than Jesus could tolerate. He strode past the second Satan who turned out to be only a reflection in a crooked mirror and turned over the table.

"For Adam!" he shouted, giving vent to anger.

Satan's eyes narrowed and as he bent over to pick up the serpentine bits that the chess pieces had become; hissing between his teeth, he raised his voice above the scene.

"Adam is here!" He pointed to his black box, snapping it shut with a heavy hand. "You too!" he added with a vehement laugh. "The fault is in the game!"

He saw the swell of Jesus' ire and this time, he wanted to crush that impertinence. That little Jew from Galilee was facing him now as an equal, daring to berate him, contradicting him, "One does not play games with God!"

He, Satan, was being lectured! The buzz was in his ear: "One throne! One God! His way with Creation!" The blast of heat was on his lips; but Satan remained silent, waving his hands in circles about his ear, as if to dislodge a troublesome insect.

"The choice is not between Good, and between Evil. The choice is between God..."

"Hold there!" Satan yelled.

"... and annihilation!" Jesus got his word in. Suddenly, there was no longer the rotund and slightly sweating bourgeois before him ... in that instant that he beheld the nakedness of Satan, Jesus understood the nature of fear without hope or alternative; and he trembled at the face of anger made total by hate, no hope for redemption ... restrained by the fate of the serpent. The anguish of the mystery was in that silent scream within his heart: was Satan not vulnerable to love?

It was akin to the first moment in the wilderness again; when answers had not yet found proper questions. The fury of the wind loosened from all corners of the desert, and the sun was swallowed up in the onrush of night. Gusts of sand rose up in swirling figures, dancing apart and together in ghosts of waltz. Underneath the baked layers of heat, the swell of pressured steam hissed through the fissures, bursting upward toward the blackening skies; shimmering down again in knifing slivers of ice and hail. Then, there was a growling, braying, cackling, yelping, whooping, snorting—a cacophony of insane shrieks and hysterical laughter ending at its apex with an appalling suspense of prolonged silence mounting in tension until it subsided with the enlargement of the rattling groans of agony of death; and, worse yet, the chorus of children in pain, tormented by endless fear ....

Jesus heard all this as an overture to his own suffering; as if all the voices of the children were his own, and awaiting a purgatory of birth ... Jesus rocked in the wind, back and forth, holding tight to the unseen hand of God.

Part 6
A PARABLE

There are such days. Grey days. Dull days. Suspended days without beginning or end. Days that are strung across time with as little drama as clothes hung out to dry. Though it would appear to be so, this was *not* such a day.

When force and opposition are deadlocked, the master at the helm is on the alert, watching the groundswells for tigers in the air and sharks underfoot.

It was not conceivable that it would last much longer into the forty days, if for no other reason than that Jesus was in the flesh, subject to the fueling needs of food and drink. The machine cannot endure the extremes of heat or cold and the exhaustion of its parts. Through the ache in the bones, the spirit must suffer, and do not imagine that Satan did not take satisfaction from the sight of those eyes in feverish fire deep inside their skeletal caverns.

"Soon, soon," he mused speaking to the air with ears. "Soon, the back *must* bend. First, the quiver; shaking back and forth, and trembling in wider arcs; then the flesh whitens, deserted of blood, draining its reserves; now, the spirit wavers for an instant, becoming ash in the flame. Collapse is complete; nothing held back for later revolt."

Satan turned to Jesus with an air of amused tolerance. "That's alright. Pray, pray, keep on praying."

"I am praying for you, Satan." Jesus approached Satan with an earnest look; one of the few times he was able to look deep inside those cynical and mocking depths. "Suppose, at last you vanquished..."

"What do you mean, *suppose?*" Satan interrupted scornfully.

"...and all is given over to smoke, and complete despair. And the beasts mock what remains of the image of God; and the darkness of Sheol covers the last of creation, dammed up in the silence of forever. Would you be closer to God? If there were no reason any more for rebellion; when all of life says 'no,' what then, Satan? Can there be a 'no' without affirmation, denial without truth! Satan without God! Even if Satan became God..." Jesus wiped the blasphemy from his lips. "...in the beginning, he must say 'yes!'"

There was that much in the thought that it gave Satan pleasure, something new and different yet startling, to be considered in retrospect. To Jesus he made light comment: "Then you will pray to *me* for mercy."

Jesus shook his head gravely. "Without that He wills it so, you have no will, Satan. Let thy will return you whence you came; wholly within His sight, Satan."

Satan laughed out of one side of his mouth then the other, making a display of broad humor for the sake of effect. "Ho, there!" he burst in on Jesus. "Balance is what you need: height and breadth and balance. From where you stand, and as far as you can see; it all fits perfectly in proper categories: good and evil, sin and sanctity, God and Satan, night and day, demon and angel, Eden and Sheol, Adam and Eve. You satisfy the twilight as the route between extremes. The sinner-saint is unknown to your mind. I can justify it in the least among men, after all, they fall so easily! I'll accept it as a convenience for kings and prophets, war is so one-sided. But you, Jesus! With me, Jesus! You may lack subtlety and the experience of centuries; I'll concede a recourse, a raison d'etre for sophistry; even the propaganda that must sound the alarm each time Adam is reborn in a cauldron without clay; but ..."

Satan shook his head knowingly and waved a finger back and forth in playful negation, pleased with his summary. The idea of bringing in the world to bear its own testimony sang out loud; it was that harmonious. Then, too, it was in keeping with that favored device where the victim participates in his own extinction; carrying his own cross and digging his own grave. He turned to study its effect on Jesus, and his brow darkened with consternation as he watched a beatific glow come over Jesus' face as if he was hearing a heavenly choir.

"God is with me, " Jesus whispered; and his voice was soft with awe and love. He need not have said one more word to convey his reply to Satan ... there was a truth above the ways of the world. Higher than all the rest was the Infinite.

"It came to pass that there was a great drought upon the earth," thus Jesus began. "The long and terrible heat had dried up all the wells and all the lakes and streams, even unto the waters hidden beneath the soil; and those who drank of the oceans, in their madness, were filled with salt.

"Thus, the common plight of man and bird and beast brought them together, even with the insects, to seek salvation. And the ant raised its head to the lion. 'Amiable beast, sir,' it pleaded, 'thy head is always nobly raised, seeking what it needs. Is there water nearby?'

'Neither nearby nor afar,' the lion replied. 'Not as far as I can see. But let us ask the same question of the giraffe, whose long neck carries eyes on a post.'

"And the giraffe who had heard from afar, lowered its neck; and, swaying back and forth mournfully, replied: 'If I could see water, would I be here, hanging my tongue between my lips? In my humble view, it is to man we must turn; whose wisdom, as we know, carries his sight beyond all our height.'

"Nor were they disappointed by man. He opened the cage where his trained hawk was kept; and let it rest on his finger while he whispered in its ear. And the hawk flew a straight line up into the highest reach of the sky; circling round and round as it descended; shaking its head as it re-entered its cage.

"How much more final could it be! There was no water; not a drop anywhere. As the animals prepared to die; even without a cloud in the sky, it began to rain.

"How unlikely! The wonder of it! Miraculous! But it was the ant, sipping on a drop hanging off the edge of a leaf, who stopped to say, 'How obvious! The Infinite! We had not thought ourselves of the mercy of God!'

Part 7
ONE POTATO, TWO POTATO

Utter fiasco. Eden was behind them. The beasts, become insane with grief and rage, were tearing at each other's flesh. Now, they had reached the other side of the great mountain, moving steadily eastward to a part of the world they had not seen before. The last word before the silence had been wrung from Adam.

"Eve!" he had cried out, and the sound of it stood between them with every range of inflection and feeling.

It was Eve who was first to look back over her shoulder only to discover that the mountain itself had disappeared in the thick mists below and the curve of the clouds above. They were never again to see what they had seen, except within scarred patches of memory where it would remain and be given to future generations in the form of a bitter restlessness and an inner goad upward to an unknown destination. Henceforth, the spirit would be alike in all that was human, making bitter comparison with the lost and forgotten experience of Eden, compelling man to the extreme limits of invention.

Adam bit back his frustration; setting his eyes forward; grimly preparing himself for any and all confrontation. He saw the world anew as a garden grown wild and given over to the wilderness of the jungle. Even the roots grew upward with evil intent; murderous vines winding around and pulling down the great trees. Every so often, out of the darkness a flotilla of cold-tempered eyes would stab him with hate and contempt. He was unkinged!

The pace of their backward flight had affected Eve even more. There was that new and startling drumming within her middle, making her feel the need for repose in tranquility; time to contemplate all the strange influences turning her sentiments toward tenderness. She took Adam's hand, and stood before him, revealing her heart: "Will we ever find our way back to Eden?"

Adam had no answer for her, dropping her hand and the question with it. However, he had seen how her girth impeded the pace he had set, so he slowed down and they rested more often.

Once more, and for the last time, Eve looked back, trying to pierce the mist. The word came from her lips with a thud: "Gone!"

"It never was!" Adam's voice was flat and final.

The way ahead was become burdensome; the prospect, bleak and uninviting. The rationale was: could there have been another choice back there? A turn with greater promise? Adam looked back, trying to pierce the obscurity. There was a hole in the mist; there was a sound of chortling; there was a familiarity that penetrated the mist. That pinched face was that of the serpent; stone cold and wrinkled; pointed fangs prancing over hard lips.

"Begone!" Adam cried out furiously. He held out his arms, opening and closing his fists, looking for a neck to be encircled by those fingers become talons.

By the time Eve had swung around, seeing nothing to warrant such offence, the serpent had re-entered the mist. She became frightened for herself and for Adam. Her voice was hoarse, "What is it?"

"Your *friend*." Adam spat out the words and with them released all that was pent up inside him; choking him as it poured out from where it had been festering. He would not speak for the intensity of it; setting his face in granite to control himself; nonetheless the tears overflowed and were visible and he shook his damp hair over his face, hiding behind its matting; ashamed, unable to stop crying.

There were no words for this. Eve merely took his great big limp hand in her own; and though his chest heaved, and he tried feebly to push her aside; she managed to croon softly to him; trying to lull him with the softness of her wordless song.

Yet it was needful for Adam to retch up all the gall within the pith and marrow of his being. The dam was breached to the edge of sanity; and what it was that burst forth was to become the *leitmotif* of the root-ends of hopeless anguish: "Was it for *this* we were born?"

Who can reply to such a question? Where are the reserves of strength when all have already been summoned up? What happens in that crucial moment of complete wretchedness when the dark abyss is all that looms ahead and the answer to life is the end of it!

Was it the love of Eve? Or that in some indescribable way, knowing that all of mankind hung in the balance, a prayer was answered? It's one matter to call it a mystery, and be done with it; it's something else for them, that instant, to have felt the soft kiss on their foreheads; the dove of peace descending, leaving behind its grace...

I PROTEST!

"I protest!" the words of Satan tore through the fabric of time, setting aside every convention that went with it, pressing against the bindings that separate the earth from the sea and the sky. The supreme anti-force whose precedent was Lucifer the Beloved, surprises us with its violence. How does love become hatred? Or, one might question, was it ever truly love, if it can deny itself to the full extreme?

"My God is not yours!" Satan flung at Jesus. "That parable of yours! Always in the last act! The rains came! Your God is the invention of melodrama!"

Jesus replied with quiet restraint: "In the end, as in the beginning, all returns to the Source."

To survive. That was all. It needed no reason. Went beyond choice. It was there....

"Was it for this we were born?" The gall had risen in Adam's throat, and he spat out its bitterness.

The rain came in smaller drops, touching their faces with the tips of healing fingers. The mist jerked upward with a flounce of curtains; and the sun could be seen.

Satan heard the opening trumpet of the new Jerusalem. He thrust against it with his shoulder refusing to believe it; blowing up with rage, summoning all the tired arguments, even some new ones, to sustain himself. "He inhales! Is that what you are saying? What kind of blasphemous God have you invented that fills Man with His breath, blesses him with freedom to choose, or not choose at all, then takes it all back! Calling it the will of God. Your God is as small as your imagination!"

"Oh, that I could contain all of Him!" Jesus whispered.

"How good!" Eve cried out, pulling Adam close, that he might share her warmth.

And Adam rose to all his height, unclenching his fists. He saw the light in the sky, and the fresh breezes drove off the burdens in his chest. He dared to believe that God was speaking again to them and his face grew soft and luminous.

"Your God is small, as Adam is small, tottering and falling at every turn; needing rescue at every climax. And your God interferes! He slams shut the gates of Eden, hides the openings in the clouds, and now Adam and Eve must die, or become transformed, like Lucifer. I protest! I beg that terrible question that only Satan dares ask: Is Adam the mirror, the image that perfectly reflects the First and the Greatest of all Imperfections?"

Jesus came forth with a sword. "What was the first sin, if not against love? What gain is there, Satan, when you cast your net for souls that what you draw in a writhing heap are dry and tasteless with all the love sucked out. What profit is there in numbers? Can you be envied the shrieks of horror when your victims waken to what they have lost? Doesn't the absence prove the glory that was its presence?

"He who tolerates thee; He who binds the wound and heals without scar; He who leans over with tenderness to raise the fallen child; He who makes the dead to rise and the fallen bird to fly again; He who opens the bud, then brings the flower with day on its petals into the lonely night of the orphan— there He is, waiting in the landscape of every soul, green, forever green and fresh, watered by love; struggling, then rising up beyond the echoes of song."

Even the hated mist had done its good work, softening the soil so that the earth lay on its back, exposed and ready for the plough. Already, spears of green were here and there like exclamation points; and in some wondrous and mysterious way, little miracles of fruit were on some of the branches, even before the leaves.

As he watched all this, seeing the reprieve; the excitement grew large in Adam, and larger: "Look, Eve! Look! How beautiful the green! The earth is a belly!"

Eve did not trust her joy, not yet, whispering to the surge of new life within her, "It is ... it must be ... Eden!"

Now, he could feel the muscles in his legs vibrate; and the thrill of the sudden flow of blood was altogether irresistible. Adam leapt up and down, clapping his hands together over his head as if to say, I am alive. Alive! His ecstasy, and the pungent smell of the wet soil overpowered him, and he romped deep into the open fields, rolling on the ground and kissing the earth like a lover. His fingers dug deep into the soil as if he would become one with it and his fingers closed over ... a potato!

The deep shadows and furrows returned to Satan's face. His eyes grew sharp, narrowing their focus to the pupils of Jesus' eyes. The glint was dangerous.

"But!" he carried the word upthrust, challenging. "!BUT!" He repeated what needed no emphasis other than to make it unmistakable that, putting extremes aside, this was the word, the perfect summation of thought and theme to describe the downfall of Lucifer, the open door through whose portals the parade began; contrariness, beating the drum; and contradiction, twirling the baton.

"BUT!" Once more, overlaying the effect. A look of triumph came floating up, despite Satan's effort to keep it under the skin; he curled his lips, clucking his tongue against his palate in an obscene sound that was meant to convey sympathy. Now, he looked as if he would apologize. He chuckled self-consciously, showing the tips of sharp teeth. Then all the warmth was gone from the desert as if the core of the earth had become frozen to give Satan the extreme accent he needed for what he was going to divulge: "the world is my victory!"

Eve had been watching Adam with joy and laughter; and when Adam came up to her, wiping the sweat from his forehead, bringing her the potato, her love was fully with him.

Together, they turned the potato over and over between their fingers; pinching it, rubbing it against their cheeks, digging into it with their nails until some of the moisture oozed out. Finally, Adam brought the potato up to his lips. He hesitated, looking at Eve meaningfully. "Surely, this is not forbidden?" he asked with an excess of caution.

Eve took the potato from him, bit into it, found it sweet; then gave it back to Adam to taste. He bit into it, and laughed; and she laughed; and all the tensions left them in a wild burst of laughter that left them both sprawled on the earth, helpless yet satisfied.

Eve spoke in a child's voice, "I think He was laughing, too."

CHAPTER FIVE
FIRST BLOOD

Eve, serpent-like, bent over and wound around
and twisted about into that loose edifice of bones
that she had called son. "Where? Where? Where?"
she screamed, "would the soul of Abel find suste-
nance?" Who can witness this sapped and grievous
flesh, and not invite death to lose its distance?
"Lord, why did You keep us alive after Eden? To
witness this?!"

Adam wound himself around Eve and they were
bound inextricably, to that green-gray mold that,
alive, had been the fruit of their love. And Adam
squeezed the milk from Eve and Eve stung Adam
with the point of her soul and together, with raging
sorrow rising wild to madness; they struck back at
God, wailing, "Not this rot and decay! Return us
*again to clay! **WAS IT FOR THIS WE WERE***
BORN?"

Part 1

CYCLIC SELF-RENEWAL

Once upon a time, as long ago as myth, in a land named Eden; a man called Adam could stand transfixed with wonder, without the measure of time, and marvel at the coordination of a hummingbird and gasp at what God had wrought in the muscular bindings of the oceans.

But the world was no longer as God had seen it. This was Adam's world, where time conspired with survival. There was death. So far, that was only an uncomfortable incident among the lesser orders of creation.

In the flawed and transfigured world awaiting the birth of Cain if another Adam had suddenly appeared, one without stain or blemish—how intolerable!

The strain, the unbearable tension, was over when Eve and Adam broke through with that first instance of sin. Afterward, the second digression was not so shocking, and the third was already forecast. But, moderation. Moderation! Keep clear of extremes and the way is never too far lost. By this token, both God and Satan were equally an embarrassment.

Of course, God was with them in a way. Hushed and invisible, muffled sounds of distant thunder presaging the storm ... Adam could not fathom this as the same God who had been so comfortable as friend and father.

The best time was at twilight, when the mysteries of the changing day brought them to silence, shoulders pressing together in the dusk; mourning as the sun left the horizon. Somehow they were never fully convinced that the sun would rise again. Lately, Eve had begun a private ritual of waiting for the first star; then rubbing her heart when it appeared, obscurely greeting the awakening life within the universe of her own depth.

Adam had learned how to bury pain in labor. There were those times in the heat of midday when, drenched with sweat, he would remember the days before poverty. Then he would kick at the hard earth, defeated and angry. But such moments were become less frequent as the moat widened between him and the past.

With the fervor of young manhood, he sought out a goal for each new day. He drew strength from vitality; and the tight set of his chin helped him over each new obstacle; whether it was to protect himself from the elements, or to seek and find new sources for water. It was still very vague, but Adam had arrived at a law of existence that was to become of major consequence to his future: get for yourself what is not given to you.

It worked. It became an adventure. These were the days of summer, each one improved on the other, giving joy to his affair with the earth. It was early morning and the smell of the dew reminded him of ... But, no! He ran over to where the stalks of corn were higher than his waist, taking the dampness to his bosom as he caressed each clump with wide-open arms. *This* was the miracle! *This*, where the unseeded soil had been. Adam laughed. And, if he had never cried before, the laughter would not have been as full and rich, as triumphant. One foot after the other in a rough-hewn dance; and he had only begun to *think* of song... when *that* shriek was hurled against the sky, flattened out over a great distance.

Adam froze. Yet, it continued, sustained, piercing, shattering his senses; reminding him of the tortured shriek of the serpent on the day of God's vengeance, and a frightened bird took the place of his heart.

"What have I done?" That was Adam's first thought as all his hidden fears came outpouring in ghastlier shapes and forms than when he had first concealed them. And the doors that fear had swung open revealed his guilt before God. The cave! Where to hide!

That shriek again! How could one breath release so much anguish?

Adam recoiled, protecting his head with his hands; momentarily expecting the fist to descend. A short wail came out of his lips, and he threw himself into the corn stalks, flattening the stems; twisting his body around when he recognized that he was not covered or concealed.

"Help!" he whispered to himself, not knowing where else to turn, and then he remembered *her*. "Eve! Eve! Eve!" he screamed and it reverberated with the nuance of a frightened cub calling its mother.

Suddenly, he stopped shouting. Just as suddenly, he grew calm. Having said the name, he knew whose voice he had heard shrieking, even why she was shrieking.

His feet would not stay on earth; he kept leaping in huge, wild circles; singing and weeping with joy. Nobody had told him, but he knew! As if the secret had been stored away from the time of the clay and released all at once, properly sprung to this very moment, *"A new life on earth!"*

Adam's voice overleapt his body, *"A new star in the sky!"* His heart drummed huge, staccato rolls; booming bass in the cavity of his chest; and there were fireworks in his eyes; his soul paraded.

Creation become Creator. Cauldron of generations; childing, new-childing the empty stage before the rising curtain. Eve held out her arms to him. She was blind with her pain, helpless, yet ready to turn on him savagely if he came not as a friend. The instinct was at hand when he needed it, to sever the foreign cord, biting off the umbilical with sharp teeth, staring dumbly at what came away in his hand, still dribbling and slippery.

With one hand, he threw the connecting piece away, that cord, whose ends have joined to all our beginnings, with the other hand, he lifted the child over his head, showing it to the sky with an air of triumph. The child showed its temper; flailing its arms, and thrashing about angrily. It resisted the tender bent of Adam's fingers, reaching toward Eve instead with a loud outcry. Eve raised her hands to receive him, saying, "He is man."

Adam returned the child to her, "And his name shall be Cain." He went outside to find a broad leaf to contain water with which to wash the child. Bending over the lake, he saw his own reflection in the water coming back clear; sharing his whisper, "I have a son."

Now, he returned in haste; sprinkling drop by drop on the child's face and body, intoning, "Cain thou art; and Cain thou shalt be!"

The green fluid was rinsed from Cain's face; tight and contorted; angrily protesting each drop of water. The features began to emerge. Cain's eyes stopped their wild turning to fix on Adam with sightless intensity.

For nearly too many moments, Adam's heart stopped beating. The blood left his face, and his eyeballs turned up in shock. He retained just sense enough to return the child to Eve, placing it on her breast, then wiped his hands with disgust. He stood this way transfixed, staring at Cain with semi-disbelief unable to credit his senses, listening to the suckling sound of Cain's lips on his mother's breast, ravenous, beastly.

Eve had not seen what had been happening to Adam; when suddenly she looked up and saw that ravaged and tortured face bending over her, foaming at the lips, breathing hate. With her free hand, she pushed his face away, screaming at him with the roar of a lioness.

Adam drew back and away from both of them. "What have we taken with us out of Eden?" he denounced her.

Eve heard him, and covered the child with both her hands protectively. Even in her weakened state, her eyes were defiant and she was ready to do battle.

Adam stood there, a man of stone with living eyes; darting, searching, moving furiously back and forth, unable and unwilling to cope with the full testimony. He had seen ... unmistakably, he had seen ... *the serpent* ... Cain was the mirror-image of the serpent!

The very concept diminished him. He was less than a child. Less than the clay in God's hand! To become a man would be to leave the boiling seas, crawl on his belly, clamber arm over arm even to see the sky, and, at last, walk on two feet upright. But upright was not yet! The spectacle had become cosmic. A swirl of forces beyond comprehension! What was this, the serpent's vengeance?! Revenge within the womb?!

Now, he was alone. More alone than he had been before Eve, and the anguish overwhelmed the terror he felt. He ran outside to the high cornstalks, where he had known more security and joy than he could remember, he hid where he knew he could not hide, flattening the stalks, and calling upward, "Father! Father!"

He was not really asking for help. Just a reply. Just to know He was there. Still alive!

Part 2
AN OMEN

The next day was the seventh. Remembering God, he rested. Besides, was it not his earliest experience of Creation? On this day, the earth lay fallow and the seed made no reach for light and water. Instead, it was Adam who burrowed; using this day to meditate and attempt communion with that strange chaos of inner landscape within his own darkness, the peaks of which were just beginning to emerge.

He took leave of Eve and Cain, seeing to their comfort; and he took his way up one of the smaller hills where he could look down and be looked down upon.

To Adam, sitting there on his smallish hill, pondering his own bewilderment, recognizing very little of what lock he had opened; it was all still as simple as the mere taste of the forbidden fruit, and its overactive consequences, so he thought. But there was a new force in the world! As he sat there; even as he ran his fingers through the ashes of the long-ago seeking more clue than he had, he was forced to recognize that somehow, in some strange way, he was no longer fully in command over every part of himself. It was as if he had left a door open, as if he had welcomed into his vital parts and given a piece of his dreams to that which was proud; not kind and friendly. Were his eyes more piercing, he would have seen that even his will was invaded; or he would have heard that other voice mocking that tabernacle within his flesh where he had hidden the memory of his Father ... even His own secret name.

That which was yet intact of the original Adam touched the answer by the tip of its feathers, not enough to hold onto; incomplete in its intimations. He felt the tip of his tongue curl up, and spat out, "What did I taste?"

Then, to the extent that he could make total confession, he admitted openly, "The fruit was gall. A drug to my senses. I would not have bitten its flesh again. Nor would I have drunk of its juices."

Remotely and vaguely, he had realized that he had altered his consciousness to no avail; gaining an underworld of truth for which he paid with the loss of his own true self; the spontaneous, natural, unafraid self that was free to range within and without itself in the merger of undivided worlds.

Adam trembled, and shook his head violently. It was more than he could bear. He had learned, by now, to save himself, his sanity at least, by going no further than he could cope with. At such an impasse, sadness was its own sea, swallowing itself in depths without bottom. It was not yet twilight, but it was best to leave. Adam knew that he had exhausted his probing. The Sabbath had ended with less rest than when it began. It would not be an easy start in the morning.

He rose to his feet heavily, and yawned. As he turned to descend, he could not help feeling that meaning had eluded him, that there were still more questions than answers.

He pulled apart the bushes to find his path, a warning rattle, and then a long, sustained whistle. Adam let go his hold on the bushes so that they snapped back and retreated with a gasp of shock.

A head screwed out at the base of the bush. 'It's Cain! My son, Cain!" Adam cried out nor could he restrain his horror at this sudden exposure....

That evening, Adam came home to Eve, calling her name through the rapid fogging of his senses, losing consciousness the moment he found her. "Bitten by the serpent!" he kept repeating over and over again until the monotony of it appalled her senses. But Eve had also been learning. She could recognize that the same words were not necessarily the same meaning. Beside the shock, she could hear questions, exclamations, surprise and revelation, incredulity with an edge of blasphemy, above all, the toppling of a king!

Verily, the wound was festering; giving off pus through a hole in the purpling skin. Finally, when it burst open, the stench was acrid in her nostrils, like nothing else in her memory.

"Bitten by the serpent!" There it was again; now sounding plaintive and bitter; the cry of the master invaded in his own domain. This time, the pathos overflowed in her heart, and she caressed his face and crooned the same soft song to him with which she had put Cain to sleep.

His eyes opened slowly, finding her gratefully; filling with tender tears. Theirs had been a different softness before. She, who had been his wife had never really been his *bride*. It was not the same. Giving witness together is not the same as sharing; and there is something that looms larger than the absence of choice or even the end of loneliness.

Since that first day, he had never broken silence again about Cain's patrimony, even in his first scream seeing Cain after being bitten by the serpent. It was as if all that had gone before was buried in some other brain whose tongue was a hole in its skeleton. It was over! And she was free to look at Adam, to kiss him where he was hurting, while her breasts grew firm and alert toward her man. Love was beginning between them.

Later in the night, while Adam slept fitfully, Eve opened her eyes, trying to penetrate the darkness, thinking all the while that it was Adam's moans and sighs that had broken into her sleep. It was then that she became aware of the other voice near the foot of their makeshift bed.

She rose up in alarm. "Demon or angel?" rumbled from the dry strings of her throat. But the moonlight was on Cain; lying at his ease, hands folded under his head, asleep with a smile on his face, mumbling words strung out without end or beginning: "bittenbytheserpentbittenbytheserpentbittenbytheserpentbittenbytheserpent."

At the same time, as if in response, with its own and less dissonant harmony, she felt the rhythmic cycle within her find its own pulse, drumming on her womb with tiny legs. Another star was entering the constellation and he would be man of woman, and he would be Abel. This new voice that had not yet been heard in the world was trying to say, *"Keep me hidden! I won't be bitten!"*

"Quiet!" She spoke to the darkness within. "Won't you be born?!" Instinctively, Eve locked her legs together, knowing without knowing why that above all Abel must be protected. She pressed tightly against her womb as if to invert the entrance, the horror possessing her that if she relaxed even for one instant, fountains of blood would spout against the sky.

"Adam!" Her shout was an accusation. And Adam woke up with his fear, "Bitten by the serpent!" he cried to her face.

Eve screamed long and deliriously, "Keep him hidden!"

Adam puzzled over her, saw how her legs were locked and how

stiff she had become, and he put the end of one finger to her cheeks, scratching the skin until there was blood. He licked the blood until he believed it had entered his own stream.

She watched this and became soothed, waiting in silence for what was to follow. "Eve." The wild went from her eyes, "In Eden," he said, amazing her with that word on his lips, "God was with us always, yes?"

He was not waiting for a reply, leaning over her with a deep-probing look, "There was a God, wasn't there?"

His voice had the unreal timbre that disowned its source, permitting itself to be shocked by its own tongue.

Eve heard him, and her body rippled. Both her hands flew up to cover his lips. "Be quiet, Adam! What if He's listening?"

Adam smiled neutrally, suddenly becoming aware of Cain's prattle; listening as if such a nursery-rhyme-homily was most natural for the middle of the night. When, finally, he did respond, it was indirectly, in a scattered way. He touched her stomach, "What else is borning?"

Her hands dropped on top of his, protecting herself should he become violent.

He leaned on her, making a hollow in her stomach. His face, at first pale, grew red, and his lips were trembling. "When we left Eden, something else was let loose in the world, something! *What was in that forbidden fruit?*"

Eve pushed him off her stomach. But he was over her, feverish and sweating out the serpent's pus: "What is it that laughs in my gut, steals the fruit of my sweat, plants thistle on the bushes, gives claws to the rose? Which voice leads me through fog into bog? Who enters my dream with a scream? To what clutch of air am I forever tempted, forever mocked with my own unworthiness?"

Part 3

THE EARTH IS GORY

Suddenly, like a sack of wind with a hole in it, Abel had folded in half.

Cain stood there, statuesque, fixed in mid-motion, the logic of the line of his body coming to focus on that intense point at the corner of Abel's mouth where the blood was trickling out. What great thirst was in the earth, sucking down each new pool of blood that formed even as it formed; carrying it all through veins of sand with a rush, subterraneously entering the waters of the ocean, salting the taste so that henceforth no throat could drink of it and not spew it forth. Yet the poison was not in the blood, but in the deed!

In Cain, the flare of the flame had burnt off the tallow. As his anger wasted itself and his nostrils ceased trembling, he could pierce the haze beyond which was the pale and waxen face of his younger brother. "Enough!" he cried stridently making as if to leave, that he might frighten the more timid one with the threat of being left alone.

He took a few steps away; but hearing no sound of movement, he hesitated. Abel was playing games. He ran, then stopped in his tracks. Still no response. Cain looked back impatiently. Doubled-up yet, as before.

Cain became uneasy. He turned about and took one hesitant step after another, returning. It was a long sleep, he decided, and he sat down beside the motionless body, to wait it out.

It was a long and painful silence. Cain kept staring with increasing horror at the constant dribble of blood. Finally, he leaned closer to Abel's ear, "Wake up! Have pity!" he finished with a shout that surely must awaken the deepest dreamer.

And the blood kept dribbling inexhaustibly. Cain scrambled to his knees and put a heap of sand over the exit, but the blood seeped through. Next, he cupped his hands, catching the outflow and pouring it back through the opening of cold teeth and stiffened lips, to no avail.

"What is it?" he murmured, "What words do I have for Adam?"
"Abel is dead."

Cain knew the voice well enough and he was happy that the serpent had appeared so providentially. However, he liked neither the
sound nor taste on his tongue of the word. "Dead? What's that ...
and what isn't it?"

He looked down on the serpent. "Strange that you should appear
this moment? What have you seen?"

"Nothing," the serpent winked, "Abel is not a word with meaning anymore. He will not be again as he was. The before is no more.
Look at his eyes! The light has gone out. Call out his name, Abel!
Abel! The air breaks before the gate of his ear. He's nothing to himself, or to anyone else. 'He' is not brother to you, not son, not man
... not even 'he' anymore, except to describe what was. Would you
put food in such a mouth?

"What will you say to Adam? Or to Eve, tugging her hair with
grief? You will say: '*Now*, there is one. Only *one*! One with the seed.
One with His breath. One to inherit the earth! Leave this thing with
the life oozed out. There is no harvest here. Nor will it sprout up
branches or bear fruit. The wind will enter its orifices, and the sun
will bloat its hollows, and the bones will fall like the sides of a tent
over what has fled to nothingness and must be put aside and hidden
so that life itself, while it lives, will not be offended and lose the taste
for survival.'"

Cain had been staring down at his hands while the serpent was
speaking. From the tips of his fingers up to the peak of his elbows,
interesting patterns of dried blood had formed red serpents, ceremo-
nial images that wriggled as he fluttered his fingers. Slowly, he raised
his hands before his eyes, searching entranced for a meaning that
eluded him. "They take life," his lips formed words without sound.

In the same trance, he bent each finger separately; then he formed
a ball, connecting all his fingers; then a fist which he shot up at the
sky thoughtlessly. Then, he remembered God.

"What have you to fear?" the serpent asked, coughing up laughter, "The whole cycle is on one shoulder now. Yours! The Future, if
there is to be a future, holds your seed in its womb."

Said Eve to Cain, "Where is your brother Abel?"

"Back there," replied Cain.

Said Adam to Cain, "The moon blooms red. Where is your brother Abel?"

"Back there among the lambs," Cain replied.

The dread lay quiet on Adam, "Is he, then, lost without you?"

Cain grew tight around his lips, "Should I have carried him?"

"He is small!" Eve groaned, "He is light!" Eve touched her heart.

Adam's hair turned white, "Is he, then, all alone, and lost in the deep night?"

Cain bristled, "The night has more peace than I!"

Adam hung like a cloud over Cain, "Tell me, then, why does the wind keep sighing?"

That shriek was from Cain's soul, "I can see the bough from whence the fruit was torn!"

Nor Adam nor Eve could say more to this; neither to condemn or to kiss their own blood on Cain's hand.

This was the night, the same night that the curtains of Heaven were kept closed, respecting the grief of the Father above and His grieving children below, seeking what was not yet to be found.

"Still the more beloved!" Cain flung his words into the darkness. Now he was restless, hopeless for peace, drawn back to the distant field where he had left his younger brother.

The night skies were thick, but he had no difficulty finding the place. A strange light hovered over the space, and the last few remaining stars were glistening in the last pool of blood that the earth could not take anymore.

"CAIN, what have you done?"

Now, he understood why the stillness had seemed so hushed and reverent. His mind was in a whirl, rebounding from fear and panic with the reminder of the serpent's assurances.

"Listen to the sound of your brother's blood, crying to me from the ground ... "

He listened to the rush of his own blood as he heard the wings of the angel of death; and he broke down; and he wept.

Part 4

A BIBLE STUDY CLASS

"Wake up, Jesus! Jesus, wake up! The stars are laughing at your closed eyes. Look how the moon glows, expecting romance ... and you sleep!"

Jesus opened his eyes with a start; shocked as always to find Satan sitting by his feet. More and more frequently, Satan had taken away his rest; choosing the deepest moment of sleep to awaken him. This, on top of his fast, was wearing on him to the point where only prayer and benediction could serve to concentrate his wakefulness.

Satan took pleasure in watching Jesus struggle to stay awake. "Such an easy martyrdom! How little I torture you!"

In truth, there was a degree of restraint in Satan with regard to Jesus: part of a game with high pretensions to superior skill or, just as likely, only the first chord had been struck; the rest awaiting the full orchestra.

"*Tonight*," he shouted with all the verve of a circus ring-master, "Tonight, something special for the aristocracy! A banquet for the son of ... Joseph the carpenter!"

Jesus was awake now; sitting up. His head was bent over his chest and his fingertips touched his bent knees. His lips moved silently. The air was in motion above his head; soon he could hear a menage of shrill children's voices, excited voices, babbling incongruously.

"This is our Sabbath, you know," Satan was explaining. "Usually, no matter where I am, I spend this night in Sheol. I would invite you along," Satan bowed graciously, "but you're underdone; not ready to ride such a mare. So! I've brought the children here! After all, if they don't study their Bible, how will they know what you're up to? Anyway, you'll forgive us if our little imps remain invisible?" Satan inquired solicitously. "You do frighten them, you know."

Now he bent backward and shouted at the air immediately above his head. "Are you all there?" A chorus of shrieking voices responded.

Satan took a long ruler out of an inner pocket, rapped it on the stone and there was silence. Before beginning, he turned back to Jesus, "You realize that no human eye has witnessed what you are about to see?"

Waiting, and getting no reply, he rapped his ruler again, and began, "Now, where did we leave our sister and brother at the end of our last class?"

What followed was a buzz of voices like animal sounds in a barn, frightened by an invader. One voice, however, rose above the others, more insistently screeching "Me! Me. Me. Me. Me!"

"Yes, Demon Gabriel," Satan named the voice.

"Escaping from Eden where God had imprisoned them!"

"Ah, yes," Satan said, thoughtfully reviewing their last session. "You'll make a Senior Demon yet! Now it's Michael's turn. Michael!"

He turned around briefly to face Jesus, interpolating, "I have honored my former friends, baptizing in their names. Now, Michael!"

Again, he interrupted himself, turning around, "The next one will be called Jesus! All right, Michael. Tell me, how did Sister Eve and Brother Adam escape?"

A frog's voice croaked: "They were bored?"

"I didn't ask why," Satan flung out impatiently. "I asked how."

After a short silence, the reply came hesitantly, "They flew under the gate...?"

"Michael!" Satan was plainly embarrassed. "What will our guest think! Men can't levitate, they make short leaps and hold to the ground. Men can't burrow, they'd cut their claws, which aren't sharp enough anyhow. Man is an undersized machine in an oversized ego. Man was!"

"...made out of mud," Michael added gratuitously.

Satan made a show of getting annoyed, "*Who* made *what* out of mud? Who invented man?"

"God, our Father!" Michael replied with alacrity. "He spat his breath out into the mud... "

"*Clay!*" Satan corrected him.

"... into the muddy clay." Michael was going to be a problem. "And! When Adam let his eyes fall open and he saw how ugly he truly was—without horns, fangs or feathery wings—God made him believe that he was different because he was beautiful: just like Himself! Now, everybody knows that God has horns and fangs and feathery wings! So God lied to keep Adam happy... "

"Not quite," Satan cut in. "But that's a bone for a higher course in theology. Let it suffice for now that man is the only animal that can lie and convince himself he's telling the truth. All right, let's hear from Raphael."

Raphael brayed with pleasure at being chosen. Not that he had much to say, but, oh! The joy of saying it. "He made two: one to pull and one to tug. The other one He called Eve."

"Good. And now, Uriel."

"They were kept hungry, but not to eat. To sing! To sing the praises of God all day, even at night."

"Raguel?"

"Then it was that God invented sin!" the words burst out of Raguel's lips like the unfurling of a great commemorative banner.

"Tell us how," Satan's voice paid tribute to the apt and succinct summary with a warm purr.

"He tempted Adam!"

"Good!" Satan turned around, nodding to Jesus, as if to say, the best was yet to come. "But let's give Sariel his turn. *How*, dear child?"

Sariel's voice was a startling falsetto, in eerie contrast to the bass undertones of the others. "He showed Adam the tree that Lord and Master Satan had grown before taking the road to the Lower Kingdom. And God said to Adam, 'See this tree which you have passed by before? This is mine! Only mine! I want you to keep my breath inside your body at peace. If my breath whispers, do not listen! If the fruit I have forbidden becomes more beautiful, turn your eyes away! Above all, do not give heed to another voice, for then I will know I am not Master in All, in my own kingdom. If another Spirit were to wander by, and speak as if He spoke in My Name, do not give heed, I warn you, for there are many who would use the name of God on their tongues that they might betray you.'

"And Adam made bold to question: 'And how do I know that it is not Thou with His name on thy tongue to betray me? What you say to me, I hear with what Thou hast given me, but where is good and where is evil, if I do not learn one from the other?'

"And God bit into the forbidden fruit while he pondered Adam's question. 'To know that would be sinful," He finally replied.

Adam was ashamed to confess that he did not know the meaning of sin; but he could see anger multiplying the wrath of God, so he did not ask.

"Bravo! Sariel, Bravo! Worthy of an Archbishop!" Satan applauded loudly. "But now, lest we forget; this moment must not go by without due credit to our holy brother and martyr, Saint Serpent. What have you to contribute to this, Jeramial?"

Jeramial made himself known in a sing-song tone somewhat between a whine and a wail, "Therefore we worship our Lord Saint Serpent for taking upon himself all the burden of Eden, though there are two schools of thought on that score: one, saying that the saint was inspired by our Prince and King; the other, arguing that it was his Unholiness, Himself, whose wit and guile took tenancy for a short term inside the Serpent. But, whosoever we disbelieve, of this there is no doubt: that He who assumes to be the original of Adam's image, He set upon our saint, persecuting him to the very roots that his limbs might not grow length again. Even then, our Serpent bethought himself of Satan, and would have called out to him but that his tongue was pulled out near to the length of his throat, and torn in twain. Yet, after the rattle and the hiss, who has not heard the far-off and heroic echo in the hollow of the Serpent's throat 'Satan! Satan!' before the twin knives pierce the enemy heel. "

"Ah, Jeremial!" There was a trace of the sentimental in Satan: "Thy father was a King on earth; and, one day, " Satan left the sentence suspended, closing off the warmth of his voice, not wanting to be trapped in vulgarity. "But, go on Jeremial. I can endure your flattery."

Jeremial spoke now in crescendos. "And why was it that our

sacred Serpent sacrificed his upward stance? That brother Adam and Sister Eve might rebel against the forbidden! And why rebel against the forbidden? *Because it is forbidden!*"The last point was made with such conviction that it rattled kind of uncomfortably with less desirable implications.

Jeremial picked up the lengthy silence, continuing the obvious route, "Just as some day, Lord and Master Satan, we must rebel against Thee. Dare all! Win all! Amen."

"Why should anyone rebel in Sheol?" Satan asked, making no secret of the dangerous growl at the back of his words. Some of the imps laughed rather coarsely; but Satan gained no further response.

"Very well," Satan clapped his hands together, and closed his eyes solemnly. "Let's say a prayer together for Brother Cain, just beginning his journey on earth..."

Complete silence. Then Satan spoke further, "Oh, that he might find his way, and receive the children of Lilith! Let each sense of him be open to indulgence; and may he find in jealousy what was not given to him that he may be full and overflowing; ready to do battle with heat and anger, letting the blood spill out to dry. Give salt to his season that his bite might be sharp. Drive him by his dreams, and let him be driven by that nature, without retreat, whose deed is justice to itself. "

Satan opened his eyes, and snapped his fingers. "Now, the closing benediction. Let's all face our guest, " Satan spun around so that he was eye to eye with Jesus and raising his hand like a chorus master, "Sprout. Sprout. Sprout. Thou seed of the fruit forbidden. May the seed become sprig. May the sprig become a forest. May there be many forests, all with seeds forbidden. Rising, rising, rising everywhere. May Sheol prevail eternally and forever. Amen."

Jesus shook his head from side to side. "Mortified spirit, leave me," he cried out wearily.

"What have you learned?" Satan challenged him, "That the difference of truth is the difference of perspective?"

"I have learned," Jesus cried out from the depths of his weariness. "Only that Hell is there where God is not. Within you, Satan!"

"What are you saying! Where is Satan *not*?" he asked, twisting the thought to his purpose. "How do you think I've accumulated so many names? Standing still?! Waiting for compliments?!" Satan snorted, and turned around. "Class! How many ways do they know me? Only on earth, I mean!"

All together they chanted, as if by rote, without accent or emotion, "Abaddon, Asmodeus, Ahriman, Apollyon, Azazel, Beelzebub, Belial, Bogy, Devil, Diabolus, Demon, Eblis, Lucifer, Mammon, Mephistopheles, Moloch, Sammael, Zamiel ... "

" ... and from Old Scratch to the Prince of Darkness," Satan interpolated, "not meant to improve my reputation." Satan laughed, then shouted at Jesus, "I am not amused!"

He became truculent. "If you know nothing else, know this: wherever God has been, *I* am!"

Part 5

THE COCK CROWED ONCE

It was macro-time in the desert. Minutes lingered, attending the hours on lame feet. The shadows grew long by half-degrees, pall-bearing night into day.

Finally, Jesus heard the crow of the cock, and he was one with the world as it had been before and would be again and forever. Another cock crowed, and the dawn was more than a will o' the wisp, more than the false light that betrays the sleeper. Now, the third cock joined to the crowing, and Jesus wakened to that wondrous sense beyond time, the magnitude that was now and will be again, the fresh bloom of the world as it was first born.

Jesus did not wonder at the summons of the cock when such were not to be found in the desert; feeling only quiet joy that the time for prayer had summoned him.

Turning to the east, however, he saw, indeed, that the three crowings had betrayed his rest. In fact, the moon was in apogee. Jesus struggled with his impatience, growing watchful, suspecting a new outbreak of Satan. For all the subtlety of his adversary, he knew that the most primitive moves were not beyond his tactics. First of all, Jesus knew he must pray; he must transcend the immeasurable pendulum that comes with silent watchfulness, drop by drop, grain by grain; waiting for what was to happen, to happen, to happen … thus, the night crunched and ground along, stringing out beyond horological mechanisms. Even as the prayers of Jesus protected him against the taut strain of an unending night, faith rewarded him with a sign beyond dispute. There was a rose streak under the black thorns where the darkness seemed most fully entrenched.

Yet, unmistakably, there was that other that clung to the roots and hugged the tendrils. Jesus could not escape the sickly smell of poisoned flowers, and cried out, "Thank you, my Father, for giving eyes to my heart that I might see the light in the darkness."

At this, the moon began its descent, at last, Satan revealed himself; humble, squat, a middle-aged man with aches and pains, looking toward Jesus for mercy. He began immediately, "Why do you want to bring harm to me? To overwhelm me and mine?" His voice ceased creaking, rising to thunder, "Destroy me and all creation topples beside me!" Satan's fury began to increase, having gone beyond caution as the remaining days shortened without ingress and trespass into this 'common' man; he began to concede that something more than the axe or the surgical blade was needed. He saw the makings of a mission in the man, that the time so far in the desert went beyond the folklore of his birth, the myth of Herod, those lost years as the son of a carpenter, even the reports from the Jordan: what had come from out the woman's womb was being born again here and was blossoming with fast and prayer to what might still be man yet more than man. "What species is this?" Satan asked himself, but would not reply "The Messiah."

At about this time, the sun revealed itself, and Jesus looked at Satan in his pitiful disguise, almost beyond contempt. Even Satan felt himself tragically reduced and closed the drama at this point.

"Wait!" were his last words that day.

Part 6

SOLACE

Was that actually a camel outlined against the stark horizon, or only some new device of Satan? Usually, this part of the desert was a desert unto itself, an abandoned wilderness scorned both by life and the non-remains of what feeds upon itself.

But it actually was a rider, obviously well off his path, and hopelessly drifting. The rider must have already seen Jesus from a great distance and was fast approaching with great excitement, stopping short just a caution's length away.

The rider observed the emaciated form of Jesus, and seeing that he was inward and distracted, dismounted and came closer. "Do you need help?"

Jesus did not raise his head and he answered slowly and sadly, "You are lost." It was a statement, not a question.

The rider squirmed uncomfortably, yet his heart grew soft toward this 'gentle madman,' as he saw him and he queried further, "Water? Salt? Bread?"

Each time Jesus shook his head to decline, the rider felt easier at heart that he did not have to share, for after all, he was lost. But he was gladdened that he had at least made the offer. "I am known as Temporus. My home is in Jerusalem."

Jesus made himself known.

"*That* Jesus! The one from Nazareth!" the other exclaimed. "The one baptized by John!" He looked Jesus over with more minute curiosity. "They're talking about you in the inner courtyards of the temple."

"Already ... " Jesus thought to himself, feeling a sudden heaviness across his shoulder blades. " ... it begins."

"You know of course," the other added in the manner of passing ships exchanging information, "they took John!" With a sharp hiss, he ran the flat of his hand like a sword across his neck in an expressive gesture. He searched Jesus' face for a reaction, noting that those large eyes showed the sort of pain than he had only seen in women at the death of their children.

He shook his head sympathetically, "I know, I know. You were one with him..." Then the thought struck him with alarm, "Then you're in hiding here?!"

Jesus bent his head in a short and fervent prayer; nor did he raise his eyes when he asked, "Simeon ben Ezra! Where will you hide?"

The newcomer stared at Jesus dumbfounded, unable to speak for a long while. Finally, he blurted out, "Oh, you mean my Roman name, Temporus: give me time!" He laughed and tried to make light of it, "They pay well for supplies, and such services."

But he saw it was not going well. He stepped back. "No magic! No spells! I would never betray my own kind!" His hand trembled as he touched the hilt of his sword for comfort.

For the first time, their eyes met truly and dug inside. And Simeon ben Ezra resisted the urge to weep and cry out for forgiveness. The words were closed off by the thin line of his lips pressed together.

Jesus spoke, directly to the man's nakedness, "I thirsted; and you offered me water. I hungered; and you offered me bread. You would have shared even your precious salt with me. Much is forgiven thee."

Simeon felt a weight rise from his soul, taking away his shame, so that the darkness left his face, and he could cry in the certain knowledge of comfort and love. He grew soft in his strength, and whispered through his tears, "Then, it is true, the Messiah?"

Having said the word, Simeon united himself mentally with all of those he had once kicked aside with his feet at the gates of Jerusalem: old men, hunchbacked and withering with their endless vigil; rabbis without congregations; young ones, green in their sap, with stars in their eyes; the sick; the lame; the ones bereft; the lepers, hoping to hasten death, beggars, wanting all or nothing, the Messiah.

Feeling the gentle lift of his soul, Simeon cast up in one heave all the demons of scorn, only to discover that beneath his mockery, he, too, had dreamed. Indeed, how well he understood the yearning, the rush of eyes toward the gate when any resplendent stranger entered. He too, with all the rest of the Jews, had stolen a quick glance.

Simeon saw himself bending over the feet of this bone-and-rag prophet. He was outside himself, looking down at himself; ready to brim over, held back by a thread, or the want of one, or that the thread should be one of gold.

Jesus had said not a word in reply to Simeon's question. Yes, a chord had been struck. The time in the desert was becoming rich with significance and Jesus was given to hear all the voices from all the corners raising a great outcry of prayer and desperate pleading, drawing on his strength, begging for his flesh and thirsting for his blood like children in the womb.

Simeon looked up and saw the face, a flame on top of a candle.

Jesus looked down, holding out his arms and Simeon felt himself bathed in warmth. He need only touch the tip of those fingers and he would be pulled up out of the swirl even as he had seen John help the new-born up, dripping with the waters of the Jordan, and smiling, and, *smiling!*

John! Terror flapped a black wing. For a moment he panicked; but even as he recognized their solitude in the desert and let himself relax, it entered his mind as a warning. This testimony was also for the cities, for the marketplace, and before the Roman idols.

He became confused. On the one hand, common sense was multiplying its reasons, adding doubt to uncertainty, reminding him of comfort and sensual pleasures. A recurrent nightmare of torture on a Roman cross that once he had seen came back just now to torment him. On the other hand, those arms were held out, still waiting to raise him ... to what glory? Those fingers were invading his insides and he wanted not to hesitate, but to cast himself into their embrace, no matter what the consequences. If only he had not hesitated that one instant before. He leaned back on his arms, keeping his distance, raising himself out of reach of those arms.

Without a word, without asking directions, abruptly he remounted his camel, kicking its sides sharply. What was wrong with this beast! It kept lagging, hardly moving from its resting place. It took much urging to get it on its way, one bent leg following the other; Simeon kicking frantically, curiously grateful that he could be diverted.

Some distance away, Simeon felt such heaviness of heart and shame that he had not even said a word of farewell that he turned around and saw Jesus watching after him, already small and remote in time. Simeon raised his hand to wave. He saw Jesus still holding out his arms to him, beckoning. Simeon forced himself to turn away. He did not wave.

Jesus knew who was coughing to gain his attention and from whence came the sputterings of repressed laughter. "He will betray you," Satan spoke matter-of-factly, without a trace of emotion. "The first of your disciples. And may this be your warning, Temporus Fugit!"

Satan laughed at his own pun but his next words were sharp and cutting, "They'll watch you perform: like an acrobat or a clown to idle away the hours. If you sing, they'll steal your music for their own voices. Show them a miracle or two and they'll fall on their faces and rise to applaud. For how long? Long enough to find the trick! What's the spell? Which words did you use? Then they'll ape you, force themselves to believe they've gotten the same results without you. The idea is to dispense with you! Who wants intermediaries? When they've emptied your bag and you're finished with delighting their eyes and filling their bellies and pulling the scabs off their sores, they'll turn on you, they'll demand more and better amusements, they'll stretch your imagination until you're prepared to suffer and inflict wounds on yourself, just to make them laugh, and laughing, believe in you. But they'll yawn at your agonies, stick tongues out at your torment and save their applause: only when you're finally torn to bits."

Jesus said no more to Satan than these few words in reply: "He would have given bread to me. He would have shared his salt with me. Water, he would have given me."

Satan sneered, "I've had my eyes on this Simeon Ben Ezra. By this time, I can assure you that you're all chewed up in his memory, you've become smaller and smaller and ready to exit. Or, who knows, he might sell you for a small piece of silver. But he doesn't matter. Of Simeon there are many, and creation takes no pride in them. But *you!*"

Satan made a sudden transition to fierce anger that spilled over like an eruption of lava, "What did you mean, forgiving sins! Who are you now: God?! Above the archangels?! Every time I take my ease before this pitiful, intolerable rabbi, he comes up with these grinders! *What* an impertinence! Forgiving sins!" Satan jabbed his finger toward heaven, and cried out: "Aren't you afraid?"

The pose and stance he had taken tickled Satan's sense of humor and he burst out into a stream of laughter mixed with obscenities, all the while slapping his sides with the magnitude of it all.

Jesus, however, was far removed from the rantings of Satan. For the first time, there on that small strand of desert ground, he felt the union of earth and heaven. All because, for a moment, even the moment that shows the future, Simeon Ben Ezra had opened his heart.

CHAPTER SIX

THE ELEVENTH COMMANDMENT

"The first, Enoch, son of Cain and repository of the seed, turned westward toward Eden to assault its heights, reaching just far enough to beget Irad; and Irad, when he was full in the flesh, forgot which way was west, and fathered Mehujael who gave sprout quickly to Metuhael; he, whose primitive passions came to stench and swamp in Lamech, in whom the strain of Cain in Adam's seed, bettered his begetter; twice, pressing the human grape dry of wine, leaving Jabal to witness the indifference of Jubal, who flung his seed to the wind; that it might come to naught; but for a slovenly cur whose bane, despite protest and pain, was Tubal-Cain.

And when the Lord and Master of Creation saw what had been wrought with the gift of life ...

He repented."

—*Satan*

Part 1
SETH

When the proclamation of Death was done, what had begun was an open grave for Adam and Eve, a cave with entrances and exits for worms and angels. But still the deed of Cain! Here's Abel, screaming his death agony (without a voice), his soul already flown to meet an undetermined destiny. Nor was the earth prepared to keep hidden and deep, having, as yet, no pockets.

Meanwhile, the time for the Sabbath neared its ceremony. Now, the sky was closing the folds of its tent, the silence lost its echo. Bless the Giver! Peace reigned. It was the Sabbath and the angels banished distractions of all kinds. Nevertheless, the question! "Then, will the seed of Cain be prime?"

When twilight came and the trumpets blew out the light, the wait had been worthwhile; unmistakably, this was God's smile, radiant with peace and harmony. The answer to Death was Seth.

It was the one hundred and thirtieth year of Adam's birth. Adam saw Seth with the shepherd's eye, whose last outcry had brought no reply; closing the gate, and cursing his fate with bitter tears, the lost lamb appears! Adam held his son close to his bosom; guarding him, the boy with the eyes of the gazelle, as would merit the best of his spirit; the best of his breath, the reply to Death.

And, Adam would sing softly, and whisper of Eden: "One will come, unstained; not a heathen; and he will be unblamed for my sin; yet, take my weight!" Once again, he adored the child, "Was it you, the young prince in rags, who came by while I was dreaming? You have Abel's face: my blessings rain on you, not Cain."

Seth understood nothing of what he had won. Eve, more wisely, had not put Cain out of her mind: the first-born lives in the heart. When the smell of blood was done and over; once more, she sorrowed.

Meanwhile, the first sprig of Adam's seed began sprouting, begetting branches that twisted and wound upward, twining its tendrils and spiraling with vain ambition to pierce the sky. Cain, wanderer in Nod, never again looked back to see where Abel's flesh hung withering; accusing, jutting bones. The bequeath of Adam's seed lay heavy in his loins.

Part 2

SHADOW OF A SHADOW

This time, Satan arrived pulling along what looked like a man-sized doll; a Petrouchka with motion but without heart. Even at first glance this curious amalgam of form and substance could be seen as something more than amorphous. Yet, it might also be described as a much abused toy, some of the stuffing lost, dragged out between centuries to perform the most stupendous trick—a miracle of coordination—that act, second only to the bite of the forbidden fruit. The trick was in the overly repetitive motion of leaning back, then forward and throwing a round object with force.

Satan had conjured up the "Shade of Cain" and was presenting him as such to Jesus.

Jesus closed his eyes, backing off, and refusing to be near the unclean shroud. Satan mocked him, "What kind of Messiah is this? Squeamish at the sight of his own ancestor ... "

"As much as Satan might yet be known as Lucifer, the star that has lost its fire," Jesus replied to Satan, "whatever *that* is, it is not what it was!"

"A proper humanist indeed!" Satan winced and as his skin had turned hard and rubbery, he was able to mimic an entire gamut of feelings, so that the truly heartless actor was inseparable from the visibly sympathetic role he had assumed. "Poor, poor leper; all covered with sores. I weep! I kiss your wounds! Oh, torment: the cries of the damned. Please, oh please, let me take the lashes on my own skin!

"Look, all of you, how noble I am! Generous and loving! Regard your Redeemer ... how he suffers for your sake!" Satan opened his eyes wide and wider, until they would seem to become all of his face, two twin lakes, hidden in the forest from the beginning of time, watching all the seasons go by and reflecting all that had ever taken place, murky in their depths, a repository of all experience and worldly insight, believing and having faith only in the passage of time. Now, his face grew wrinkled, the leathery rills like the concentricities of an aged redwood, and his voice rang like a rusting and cracked bell whose bronze tolling nonetheless dominates the landscape, "You would die for them, for such is your bent ... but *would you become them?* Small, weak and mean, forever bickering, dwarfed by appetites ... petty sins, petty virtues. Would you give eternal life to *that?"*

This was not the same Jesus who had first entered the desert. Now he had seen and spoken with Satan and it had sounded an alarm which, while adding fear and contributing caution, had also brought new insights, even respect, that man had survived this long. But more! The isolation, the fasting, the prayer; that purity of love and devotion to God in these desert days: the harvest had come full. He was able to pierce all the veils surrounding Eden, and see the world as it had been before the disobedience, the colors as they really were, the smell of the air without decay or death and, knowing joy in its true state each time like the first, fresh and forever surprising delight, never seeing shame or feeling guilt; alive to every instant with innocent and unquestioning faith, knowing always that the sun would rise, and no harm would come while love grows stronger, here was the universal, the true work of God!

With all this firmly in his depth, what had seemed like a wall between himself and Satan during the early days in the wilderness had now become the one and only Holiness, against which the cavil of Satan was demeaned, bringing evil beyond insanity in contrast.

In the eyes of Jesus, Satan had returned to that same primal darkness from which the hovering Spirit had brought forth the light. "Satan! What of the clay that did not feel the breath of God? What of those who hid from the light, thinking they might not be seen there when the eye of God was turned that way? Should one find soul where there was none? Even where the soul has been and is no more: shall we do aught than commemorate that which gave it passage; so that again risen from the dust, it may once more contain a more purified and chastened spirit. Satan! That which you call the "Shade of Cain" maligns the precious vessel that was the first son of man! I find evil where the shadow remains past the departed form and is no longer bound by its presence. That which goes against nature is against God. How dare you speak for Cain!"

"Who then, speaks for Cain?" Satan asked, not of Jesus; but turned toward the moving shroud. The voice without tongue rasped and groaned under its cobwebs, having not made sound for so long. "Satan!" finally tortured its way out.

"No!" The voice of Jesus thundered and the strength of his spirit was shattering in its power, considering the feeble state of his body. "Remember the mark of God! Return to your silence!"

"*I* speak for Cain!" Satan raised his own thunder. "Let Abel accuse, if anyone must. *You* raise him up! *You* open his lips and give a hearing to his protest. Let him fill the sky with complaints: 'You were the intruder! You came between Cain and Adam; between Cain and Eve; between Cain and God; between Cain and his inheritance!' What happens when the watchdog bites the interloper? Should we find fault with the dog? Or with the dog's Master, that higher intelligence that provokes action and reaction? Can a fish walk? Who put murder into Cain's heart?"

Jesus intoned, "I can hear the sound of his brother's blood crying to me from the ground..."

Again from the ghoulish lips: "That's what God said to me."

The Holy Spirit was within Jesus, who began rocking back and forth, exuding prophecy. "And God was merciful toward the lonely child that sat within Cain, taking away his bewilderment, that he might expiate his terrible crime..."

Satan snorted, "Does His might need sight to prove right? Does His sight need right to prove might? Does His right need might to prove sight?" He pressed his point, "Neither Cain nor I have the least desire to make a case of extenuating circumstances. To do that much would be a concession to the view that holds Cain accountable. Look! How easy it would be to enter such a plea: Who would *not* overflow with passion at each new threat of expropriation? Then, think of the exodus from Eden; the unborn child luxuriating in that thick richness from his mother's body, suddenly grown thin, stopping and starting sporadically, the substance of wrinkled fruit clawed and scratched from the miserly soil. After such a trauma, what is there to apologize for?" Satan shrugged his shoulder, and turned away.

"Are you saying that Cain is neither more or less guilty than the stone in his hand? Can the stone say 'yes' or 'no?' Had Cain no other choice than murder?" Jesus paused, shocked by the very proposition he had interjected. "Shall we awaken the wrath of God to witness?"

Satan fumbled briefly at this; but came back with a *pronunciamento*: "I call Adam and Eve to witness!"

He glanced sideward at Jesus, smiling to himself at the other's appearance of alarm, as if the earth was about to regurgitate. Satan extended the game awhile longer, looking down by his feet in silence; then he resumed his conversational manner, "So they had their first taste of human death! So they found it too strong a brew! So they sent their first son into exile, making him private to his own agony!"

His sentences skipped along; each one a grasshopper, from a sitting position. In such easy manner did Satan establish his premises, why bother a challenge? But what was this? With an abrupt change of pace, Satan was turned heavy and fierce, pounding out a whole network of spectacular conclusions, " If Cain is his Father's harvest, which Father reaped Adam? Who taught Adam? Is there a difference between Cain in exile and the refugee from Eden? *The breath of the breath of the breath!* Remember, Jesus, in the beginning, always, in the beginning. Cain and I know something about origins. Dare I breathe the name you dare not whisper? If the Absolute is what you want without which you will not be satisfied ... be ready to stand convicted!"

It was too far-gone to challenge Satan's premises. Satan had already scored an important point for himself. Jesus was incensed, "Your mouth is a nest of serpents, Satan. When you open that pit as you have just done, I can see all their loathsome bodies; waving and twisting and turning over ways to distort the truth. Yet it remains! The smell of blood is in the earth yet! Who has Abel's blood on his hands? While all your forked tongues dart here and there and everywhere but to the core: if Cain has no guilt, what is innocence?"

At this moment, a strange and unintelligible moan came from the 'Shade of Cain', as if it would say its own piece. But Jesus would not give it that respect, nor would Satan trust any reply other than the one that burst from his own lips, "With all your false humility and devious moral strictures, do you dare speak to me of twisting tongues? How you would prejudice the court! Make your case, if you must, without bringing bloody hands to drip on the great table while you shout: 'Murder!' The event is not itself! Not its own origin! And I won't have you handling the presentation with an appeal to fools and your own race of self-hearted morale-builders!

"My gentle enemy! I see you now, sly and soft-muscled, afraid to wrestle me, knowing my greater strength, but, teasing me, stroking my fur, while you guide me inside your cage. Stoking my flames, forcing me to flare until I settle on the springs of my haunches, all set to catapult, and, all at once, the music changes, and you put me off with angelic hordes singing non-aggressively.

"Then, once again, you turn me from force, and I become the game-player whose vanity must suspend all brutalities, subjugate the irrational axe to the courtesies of skill and superior strategy. Look at me now! Curtseying and giving back-handed compliments to this skinny pretence of a prophet, implying the worthy opponent!

"Why and why are you? Really! Bringing me so often to the brink! Can you imagine that I have not learned that technique? And then I have to watch you sitting there so unperturbed; in your own primitive way, fanning my flames, bringing me to a peak, hoping, as the fire rises, and the burn rages I'll be ready, vulnerable and ready, *ready to confront Him again!*

"Is that your tactic: let one destroy the other, and you take the hindmost?

"Let me tell you something, Jesus. This case is not going to trial. Fill it as you will with bloody hands and the perjured evidence of Eden, this case is not going to trial. And I'll give you a hint why. There is no court, Jesus. That's why. Yes, we have a Judge. I confess, we have a Judge. But He must always excuse Himself. You might get him to put on His robes; even to roll out the Law with a few thunderbolts. But in the end, He knows! And I know! In the beginning, was pride, that pride was Creation, until the flaw! And now, every law, every commandment whose life was to hide the flaw, to exonerate the Judge, *speaks guilt!* Everything is as it was in the beginning. And not even myth can change a piece of it: the forbidden fruit is off that tree!

"If you would know the humility of Satan, in all this time have I said a word to you about what *didn't* happen during the six days? Have I ever tried to make you curious about the last day, the one you call the Sabbath? Why the curtains closed so ultimately! It's all in the fruit, rolled up in a ball and expected to be forgotten. Adam knew it. Eve knew it. By the time the secret reached you, Jesus, it had spent its shock, been forgotten, or distorted, or made contrariwise. But for some, the stink is pure! That's what I have to say, and you might well listen to me, while the oyster shell is open, and the white pearls are yet visible in the swallowing night. Listen! And venture the thought that He must have known the insides of His own invention ... the fruit being bitten; that great and fearful Revelation, the 'bloody hands!' that too, if you must. Listen closely, Jesus. I'll drop to a whisper, not to frighten you too much. Also, I'll let it fall in kindlier tones than the full truth will bear. It's not my intention to destroy you with knowledge, or make you mine in servitude to the one and only. You seek within the universe. You would scan the stars, Listen!

"*I am not my own invention.* Do you hear that? Could Satan have invented Satan? I am as much the court jester as Adam, as *you!* We play our games with their intricate moves; each believing his own role. While we slept, the costume fittings were being made, and every actor awakes, *believing he is himself.* And if that awakening after sleep has any merit, it's in discovering which role is not a role; the one before the great sleep.

"Meanwhile, I have learned why I was chosen. I, the brightest star in all the constellation! I was chosen, given the role of Satan to play, because, if there were no Satan, (lean your ear closer now. Suck it in!), if there were no Satan, *He* must confront *His own* Imperfections!

"Stop it!" Jesus cried out at last, having listened to what he would not have believed could be said so blatantly without, at least, the heavens falling. Now, he understood the patience of God. Either that, or...

"You must listen!" Satan continued insistently. "This is the dark side of the sun, the side that chills and chafes the meat. At almost the close of the forty days, or perhaps to the close of eternity, you have chosen the impossible way, the abstract signs and symbols. Heave them away and listen, It's not arcane. It's really simple. I am simple. God is simple. There are many Messiahs, but only one of me. That's what keeps us at pure extremes, not good and evil, as you think.

"Only the pure selves, undiluted, and not confounded by confusions of source—excuse me, capital 'S.' The Source is power! *His breath!* That which he wasted on Adam, inherited by Cain. Are you getting it? Source/Breath/Power: the trinity that keeps the universe in motion; names its own environment; assumes its own inevitabilities, even to overlook the imperfections that are invisible to the many Children of the Breath whose business it is to adore the Source."

Jesus was now beyond patience, even beyond the marvel of God's possession of it. He had to confront the images that Satan was hammering on the tabernacle, the biting words of blasphemy, exceeding its offence, "Then say it Satan! Let out the last of the filth ... that God is the murderer of Abel!"

"It's on your tongue," Satan replied flippantly. "Then give me reply to this, if you can," Satan rubbed his finger across his nose in a quick contemptuous gesture. "Tell me this: would Cain have slain Abel in Eden?"

A frightening sound came from the 'Shade of Cain' this one, obviously, of its own will and from its own necessity. The dust had established itself, and was seeking substance. At the end of pity, somehow the lost soul had whispered through the dust, "How could I have known, the stone, when thrown, was prone to death?"

At this, Jesus bent his head, respecting the immensity of suffering that had fashioned a tongue for itself.

"Abel, he ... at least, he ... was planted in the sky," the voice continued grotesquely.

Jesus spoke quietly, measuring his words with care, "What is this, Satan, that even the dust you scooped up with your hands must speak! That, which goes by the name of oblivion, has found an echo in the long ago; even thus, seeking favor and grace of God; even from the dust, crying out its conscience. Where is the wind for this long sigh if it is not that same breath, once from God, befouled on your tongue?"

Satan, too, grew quiet, recognizing as well that the time was become crucial. "You speak the word 'God' as if it were your own possession, a monopoly peculiar to yourself. And while the same word is on our lips, my image is not yours, nor have we the same convention of meaning. I will grant you validity (and this is why I have not debated it with you previously), I will grant you validity only as far on earth as you can walk, and as far back as you can remember with your own mind. In this piece of time, within this space in the universe, this that you call 'God' is accurate to the sight of a mite in a puddle, a bird in a cage, a frog in a lake, an ant on his mount. Jesus, I have looked beyond the rim of the universe!"

"Is it then the enormity of your vision of God that justifies the immensities of evil?" Jesus asked, to which Satan smiled and nodded approvingly; seeing the complex reasoning that had opened the kernel with one blow.

Then the smile froze on Satan's face and drained off. "I may be able to speak wisely of cosmic events, but why I was brought here to this meeting, I will never understand!" He slapped his sides impatiently. "So be it! More than likely, I am here so that I won't be elsewhere, where events of greater significance are taking place," Satan's eyes twinkled shrewdly. "I assure you, the role of Adversary is not an honorary degree."

Now, the humor, too, had drained away. His eye fell idly on the Shade of Cain, and he looked from it back to Jesus. "Consider my servant Cain. He serves my moment, yet you would not believe that I serve God by serving Cain. Who else? When the earth began to vomit blood at the feet of Cain and the trees bent away, and the animals fled with horrible groans, was there anyone more alone in the universe, except for the serpent? When Cain was in his anguish, screaming, trying to hide from God, did Adam come running? Where was Eve, mother to man, but hiding in the privacy of her own grief? That terrible day when God held court; Himself judge and jury; and Cain crying from the roots of his tongue for total death, not diminishment: to become less than the original clay as if there had been no genesis. And who was there to defend Cain?

"With my own ears, I heard the outcry of his soul trying to escape, confronting God: 'You favored Abel's lamb over the fruit of my fields, so I gave you Abel's blood instead.' And when the truth was given voice, the thunder swallowed itself, and there was just enough mercy to be cruel, to cause Cain to forever seek the shadows, to become a wanderer over the soil that would remain dumb to his pleas, never again to share its fertility with him. With my own eyes, I saw the smoke as God burned into his brow a single letter of His own forbidden name, to stay the hands of other Cains, leaving vengeance to Himself, leaving His mistakes in my hands. Why to me, Jesus? Ask yourself if you have seen that much of the One whom it pleases you to call 'Father.' To be blatant: Adam left Cain to His Father; his Father left Cain to me!"

Satan covered the shade with his cloak, "It is my talent to adopt lost causes. My eye is to the impure and the imperfect. It's not so pernicious to show off the flaw. Yet I am tolerant. It is unfortunate that His penchant for uniformity is contradicted by the very nature of man. But, didn't He leave His breath behind? Am I alone in saying no? Sometimes, I think man exceeds me! But because I've seen the almost-perfect, my eye is keen for the flaw. Do you really think that ears are closed in Heaven when I dare a question or two? Look at me, Jesus! Tell me. Am I a singer of hymns in a chorus? Could I be less than a *soloist?*"

The Shade of Cain moved backwards without will and Jesus had a last glimpse of the shivering form from which the soul had fled. The shroud fixed itself in his memory to reappear again and again in his prayers. Long past the forty days, Jesus would see this shroud invisibly covering the rich garments and jewels of the vain and the proud; the last gray tent over darkening souls.

"Back to the potter's wheel!" There was Satan's voice again. "Back to the dust…"

"To another judgement!" Jesus raised his voice to its height. Whether Cain heard is uncertain.

Part 3
THE ELEVENTH COMMANDMENT

A platform of hot sand, a few rising boulders, and two figures sharp-edged in bas-relief, shimmering in the heat. That's all. After such a statement of conflict, at least an arena with a panoply of clanking crusaders! Some bright colors!

Yet see what served the drama, no black-flamed messengers, just the fixed and unblinking face of the sun. It served Jesus well. His were inner climaxes. But for Satan, who by this time recognized every grain of sand; here was boredom verging on apoplexy. For one whose range was the ends of the earth; whose great game was to hide in crowds, picking off his targets, taking pleasure in malice, dominating the circus, the spectacle, always with an entourage, what scene was this in the desert!

Jesus, with his keen eye, had understood all the whirl and frantic commotion. He saw that Satan could not be alone to himself; that he could not abide tranquility. Not for Satan the idle range of contemplation, without purpose or direction.! And Jesus understood the drift that Satan feared with such violence, that he must always be in control.

Wipe out sentiment! Pour out the slops of sickly memory! When Satan became restless, which was more often the fact than not here alone in the desert with Jesus, his anger and hatred was such that it also turned upon himself. Jesus had witnessed one such moment when Satan tore into his own flesh, mocking himself, "And I was going to stand apart from Creation, to show Him where He strayed! And they were throwing the word 'love' at me! And I told them about love, the only true love. *I* am the lover! *I* have the taste for perfection! Let the whole thing be translated all over again!"

As if that were not enough, there were those moments when Jesus would give him that special look, that brittle-wise, peasant-sense lift of the eyebrow, an insolence that would seem to intimate, 'You have lost your mystery.'

For Satan this was an abomination of the most unbearable sort; for, if he valued nothing else, this was it: Satan the enigma. Satan the inscrutable.

From that moment on, Satan pursued Jesus, poked and prodded, hoping to provoke this 'insight' out, where he would demolish it. The time came, and finally Jesus said, "Lord Satan, is it! I recognize no majesty here! Only a creditor. A petitioner. More than anyone, dependent on God. You speak of the power of Satan? I call it gall. Pretense! In all this dialogue about beginnings, about Creation, *you have one word to speak*. It trembles on your lips. You try to whisper it. But nothing happens! That's because God has not yet said His 'Yes'. So there you are, waiting pitifully, practicing your degeneracy, full of tragic conceit. Lo, God speaks! And where there was emptiness, life begins. Your moment has come! 'No', you say, and you grow big with sin. 'No', you say, expecting the flower to turn away from the sun, to spurn the rain, and fold in its petals. Say 'No' once more, Satan, and see if the fish leave the sea; if the birds never use their wings again, and all the trees drop their leaves, "Your way is with man, Satan. Man has heard your 'No' and it covered him with a net, and he found a way to fold in his petals, to leave the sea, to lose his wings, and drop his leaves. Man can say 'No' to God.

"The flower, the bird, the fish, the tree, they return to God *only* what they have received from Him. But what about man? Need I tell you what happens, Satan, when the heart ripens and deceit is pierced and the unnatural becomes faith; when man says 'Yes' to God, he will be returning *more* than he has received... "

"Ah, Free Will again!" Satan cut in arrogantly. He raised his eyes with mock piety. "God took a risk, did he not? First with Adam. Then with Eve. Let's even concede that they overcame temptation, even that! Would Cain?" Satan smiled. "Will someone please stand up and admit...I would have bitten the whole roll-call of generations!"

Satan gave Jesus an enigmatic look. "Forget it! I say that the greatest and most pretentious, the most gullible and naive aspect of this Free Will is that it is. The stars are fixed in orbit; the sun has its course; the sea, its bed. Why man should have a hand in his own destiny is beyond me. The saint with his sacrifices is as unhappy as the sinner with his indulgences. The ones in between are afraid to live. So where's the happiness? So that he can say 'yes' to God? Nonsense! That kind of 'yes' is a bribe; no less than the promise of Paradise; an Eden with forbidden fruit; and he won't be able to say 'no' again. Sweet 'no!' Sweet freedom!"

Satan was becoming more and more excited, almost jumping up and down as he made his point. "He gave them His breath, didn't He? He took the risk, blowing part of His own soul, filling balloons of skin with pride and pretense. Now that they're blowing in the wind, how does he bring them all together? Judgment Day!"

On Satan's lips, it sounded obscene. "I see it! I see it! The puff and flame of smoke that ends it all!" Here, concentrating his irony, he brought his face close to Jesus, nose touching nose, and spat out each word so that it sizzled with his full contempt, **"Bringing the world back to where it would have been if He had not allowed Free Will … if, in the beginning, He had kept His breath where it belonged."**

In the whole of Satan's diabolic range, what was most convincing to Jesus was its transcendence over mere inventiveness. What issued as insights scattered carelessly over a wide area, was more than spontaneous; more than the flotsam and jetsam from a prior shipwreck. No. These segments were from a working plan, a blueprint of intentions, the architecture of Satan's future reign. When Satan spoke of Creation as a ridiculous circle that returns where it started, what was Jesus to reply, after tamping down disbelief that the work of God could be so minimized. Loving God to the last breath, the last drop of blood, would it not grate against the grain and rouse the fiber of every nerve, merely to imagine that God could be humiliated or despised, even by the likes of Satan? Yet here was Satan, saying, "Your God is a horse, a cow, a dog, a kitten, a domesticated animal who chases intruders, carries you on his back, and gives you milk, Your God is not my God!"

And Jesus listened well to this, shuddering, the prickles of his flesh rising; his soul in torment. Who could hear all this and not feel the power that breaches the pitiful armor of man to revel in chaos? Why should God permit this unequal struggle? Does not the overwhelming power justify the collapse that ends in sin?

First was Faith, *that* Jesus knew with all his being. Then there was Responsibility, which included reverence toward the Source of Holiness, as well as respect and love for that which retains His breath. Even if man has fallen in the swill, inevitably, he must raise one eye away from the crapulous slime, and when that eye is raised, Jesus told himself, "It must seek a star!"

In a sudden moment of exaltation, the blessing like strong wine coursing through his body; Jesus sank to his knees, trembling with the open secret that had just been revealed to him: "Death has lost its sting!"

And to Satan, who regarded him querulously, seeing a benediction without rhyme or reason; to Satan, he shouted: *"For this I was born!"*

Satan drank it all in, as usual, looking for clues, or a soft middle in which to strike the first blow. "You must have heard God weeping," he commented wryly.

Whatever there was of ecstasy in Jesus, as his mission began to carve itself on the face of mountains, had something of wildness in it, too; an enthusiasm that brought him off his knees, approaching Satan with burning zeal, petitioning, "Bring me inside your darkness, Satan! I carry no light with me. Nor will I hold the hand of God in prayer. It is true, as you said, that I have heard God weeping. For whom does He weep more than for those unfortunate souls who have lost any resemblance to Adam? I can hear them, too, Satan. Night and day without rest, the desperate pleas, the unceasing shrieks of the wretched and the damned."

"Are you saying that I have unhappy guests?" Satan amused himself with haughtiness. "Did I hear you begging to enter Sheol?"

"Let me try to bring them solace. There is hope, Satan. Even with Cain, God was merciful. Even when the limbs are broken, the tree grows new branches."

Satan scratched the tip of his nose, and looked at Jesus with forced tolerance. "You'll earn yourself a martyrdom yet!"

"It's not that, Satan. Hear me out! I say to you: If, because I have lived, one man goes to his knees and blesses God; one man, who might not have knelt otherwise, if one soul repudiates evil, and rises to the light; if only one child remains unharmed; if one old man faces pain and loses his fear of death because of me; if one sick diseased soul hears the song of angels and takes up his burden with joy; if one voice among the many is comforted, and finds trust enough to take up my cry: 'Forgive and be Forgiven, Repent and be Redeemed' then I will not have lived in vain."

"Brave words!" Satan applauded. "You know the length of flesh and bone; have you seen the size of the spirit?!" He lashed out forcibly, "Fly on those short wings of yours, while you have time! Visit with me in Sheol! Indeed! When you come, you won't be just visiting! It will give me special pleasure to show you the Abels that vanquished the Cains! In your simplicity, there is only one category, *there*, you'll see the ones that barely fell short of Heaven — the choice ones who begin by crying for total death and we indulge them in sin instead. You and your categories would be overwhelmed by the distance a little unexpected pleasure can travel.

"Forget the torture racks. We go a longer way without the kneading, the molding, the re-casting in the fires. You've never seen a man without a conscience, what you call a sense of guilt. Give them the freedom of the senses, without that eye watching them, even the saints take a swig and dance a jig. I don't command! They obey! The flaw, you know," Satan finished casually.

Jesus concentrated intensely on what Satan was saying; having recognized well into these dialogues that there is a negative side of truth which needs only inversion to complete the puzzle.

"Free Will!" Satan was jibing him. "If the fault is not in the stars. If 'original sin' began with the serpent. If the 'original thought' was not Eve's or Adam's. It all sounds so beautiful, so idyllic, saying 'Yes' to God. Wouldn't you say, however, that the alternatives were *slightly* loaded: with expulsion and death weighting one side of the scale? Not even a warning what the punishment would be! 'If you eat of the fruit that I have forbidden thee, your lives shall run a quick course and you shall awaken no longer in Eden.' "

Satan gave Jesus a quick sideward look, "That's why you're here, isn't it! To help expunge the workings of a hasty temper: to recast guilt into something more palatable. Mercy and forgiveness and love, for example?"

Jesus was hearing the massed voices of the suffering reaching a crescendo, tearing at his ears at the same time that he was trying to pay heed to Satan. It must be said that Jesus had to shake off even that breath of doubt that Satan nurtured, knowing too well how even that breath stirs the gossamer fabric of sin. Intuitively, he knew better than to try to follow Satan through those circular labyrinths of the rational. Here, no doubt, Satan was past master of the innuendo, and those ingenuous questions that obscure the thread and lead to a center without entrances and exits. The object, as Jesus well suspected, was to circumvent those portals that only faith can open, to reduce all mystery to a formula, a science that would not provide for non-answers; speculate in space without the comfort of dimension. Whatever didn't fit the test-tube was superstition!

Jesus replied more to the massed voices than to Satan, "Each dawn, my Redeemer comes to greet the light."

Satan was utterly confounded. Jesus had gone far beyond in his reply, though on the surface, it would seem that he had not really crossed paths with Satan. Satan shook his head, "I can see that I have been setting a mousetrap for a lion..." He sat down at Jesus' feet in the manner of a storyteller, making circles in the sand with his finger. "When God first sent down the tablets of his law; there were eleven in all. Try as He might, there was room for five on one side, and five on the other. Try as He might, one would have to precede the rest; or follow the others. That would not be possible; for God understood that the one that preceded would loom greater in significance; and should the same commandment follow the others, some scholar would be bound to call it an afterthought of lesser importance.

"Thus, it became a matter of deciding which of the commandments should be omitted; because, as you well know, Jesus, above all, God likes order. For God, the choice was simple. There was one commandment without which the rest were meaningless. Simple trivia! This one commandment was so far above the rest, that it had been already written in the first clay; and, certainly was part of God's own breath, which woke Adam to life. It's the one commandment that animals share with man equally for it had not to be learned; nor could it be maligned.

"And God said what had to be said, for there was no other way, "Let us not write down this law, which is above all laws, beginning as it does, and ending as it will, with Life. Let those who go mad, and those who choose not to follow their soul be stricken with dead eyes and wander in Bedlam. The rest need no such commandment. I say to you, and to all that can hear, that precious truth which is now all of nature. I say to you: **Thou shalt survive!**

"And that was the eleventh commandment, Jesus, the one you have scorned and is now in your stars. I tell you, Jesus, you are betraying your old age. More, I cannot say!"

Then Satan was gone, leaving a sudden chill behind.

CHAPTER SEVEN
THE UN-CREATION

Eden lay awash.

Would it ever be as if it had never been?

Which flood of which waters carried the dust that had been the grace of Adam, the beauty of Eve?

The taste of timelessness was sweet in the calm and stately silence.

—Satan

Part 1

THE DEATH OF ADAM

Six days and nine hundred and thirty years after the great COM-
MAND proclaiming the hour of sunrise for all of creation; it came
to pass that he who was born to live forever, Adam, was dying.

At first it was as if a giant redwood had fallen over, splintering
down to its roots. But it was Adam, lying on his back, chest heav-
ing, cheeks ballooning out, then sucked in hollows as he struggled
with the air entering and leaving his lungs. Meanwhile, his hands
scraped and shoveled into the soil, seeking a handle. Meanwhile, his
feet pedaled the air awkwardly, without grip; jerking convulsively at
intervals to kick off the amateur Angel of Death bearing down on
him.

Adam was yet in his youthful strength, which was not a mercy,
prolonging his agony with short fits of recovery. At last, exhaustion.
His legs fell with the sound of a bass drum, conceding the end of his
will.

Even then, it would seem that the Angel of Death had neither
grace nor experience enough to finish it with a flourish. The body
had bitten into the soil, but the soul had not yet found its exit.
Clumsily, the Angel of Death shook the loosening flesh; but not
enough to open the gates. The soul was still shuddering within;
refusing to let go; not believing the long time between heartbeats.
Adam's finger pointed upward.

Again, the crunch. Adam's body was slightly levitated and shaking violently. A blind look entered his eyes; the harp strings were at
their last quiver in his throat; the tips of his ears whitened; his lips
loosened their touch; his teeth, their bite; and his jaw fell and sagged
against his chest. Suddenly, he lifted his head; his face trembled, and
the eyes took on force even in their whites. His fingers scratched
again at the earth and each hand held a fistful of sand that it flung
into the sky, complaining. Then, it was over. A soft whistle of air

came up from the very depth of his lungs, and the tongue flattened itself to slide past the foam-flecked lips. The soul of Adam followed. The first man was dead.

Overhead, the first witness. A raven flew by, descending in small and smaller circles, fluttering crazily and dropping one black feather to float down near where the body lay spread out and bound to the earth like a prisoner.

The little black beads of eyes beheld the graying clay and, remembering that this was the image of Him, who gave life to them all, it cawed and shrieked, gone mad with shock and grief. The alarm it raised in the silence of the fields summoned other ravens to the scene, and then the doves joined the ravens, hanging suspended and reverent in an awesome cortege.

It was the silence that summoned Eve. The earth was as it was before a storm, heavy and brooding. Yet, there were no clouds. Only the white and black birds floating in slow circles over the distant fields where Adam had gone to meet the dawn this very morning.

When she came to the place, she saw it all at once and her eyes started from their sockets. She looked from the body upward, and asked her question, "Have You taken back Your breath?"

She seated herself beside Adam, staring long at the face that did not remember her. "Adam. Is this your clay?"

And as she sat there, lost and spellbound, in another part of the world, Cain awoke suddenly within the darkness of a dream, and screamed at the vision. In a rush of wind, Eve heard him, heard the voice of her own crying child, yet she could find no lullaby. Not even a song for grief.

The night was coming and Eve left as she was: calm and totally composed, without a backward look. In faith, surely Adam would be there, asleep in their bed ...

When morning came, she rose from the cold and damp ground, fatigued with listening and waiting, now certain that he would not be coming.

Back to the field she went. Back, where that which remained might be called Adam. She tried not to look there and release her grief. And she trembled at what was storing up inside herself.

"God," she asked quietly. "*Was it for this we were born?*"

Once Adam's dominion; the earth spread open its dusty arms to embrace his remains; the worms blinked upward and dug deep. As the gape received its fill— a thud! — a plop! —shivering, rippling the fields; that great throat which had called the dust to nobility; that great throat burst forth with an outcry that shook the foundations.

One sob, then silence. And this time, this time only, respectfully, the worms withdrew from the pouch that would be Adam's. And, the angels capped their own tears, reserving the whole shawl of sorrow for the woman alone on the fill.

Eve spoke through the tightening shoulders of sand: "ADAM, where do you hide?" She bit the earth, as she had bitten the fruit; then, mouth full of sand, tore at the roots of her breasts, inconsolable.

Those late years, love had become Eden; and, there was no Eden without Adam; thus, her soul sought exit. And the rib moldered with the skeleton, rejoined for eternity.

Part 2
ENOCH

In the interval between destinies, Adam's daughters and the sons of Eve concerned themselves with genealogy, and they scattered like seeds in shifting winds; bulking man and womankind.

First, the land within sight of the seas was invaded. Then, wherever one could nudge streams, lakes, and rivers; then, at the place where the forest ended; and, above the underground flow; plains and valleys; then, from the lowest foot of the mountains, upward; until, finally, wherever the land was, there, regardless of heat or cold or shifting sands, the humans scrambled and skirmished to occupy the precious space.

Tubal-Cain. What is that strain of kings, waiting in the wings? See the clay, turned to mud, fingers stained with Abel's blood, flaunting on their brow the sign that God had made a vow!

It was not a dream, one night to the other, repeating the scream when Cain killed his brother! Begot and beget, but never forget, take heed! The deed has entered the seed.

Abel left Abel behind. It was Seth, in default of Abel, it was to be Seth and his strain of the seed, that would unroll the other furl of generations. It was Seth, and the incidence of murder, that introduced Enosh. And Enosh waited eight hundred and fifteen years to father Kenan; who, in precipitous precocity, conceived Mahalalel when he was only seventy!

Abel left Abel behind. It was the turn of Jared now, whose life commemorates a blessing in the birth of the one who walked with God ... Enoch!

Abel left Abel behind. The childhood of man was over. Innocence had departed with few regrets and when Enoch took his entrance, the awesome and wondrous chords whose theme was the new and the fresh from the hands of God were already forgotten. There were none left to wander the earth cradling that memory, to sing the loveliness of new-birth in the morning dew of Creation. There was no reason for reverence, and, without reverence, why turn the foot aside before stepping on the flower?

Unfortunately, it was to be a prolonged and seemingly endless adolescence. Those who came later plundered their elders, seizing what needed seasoning, bringing passion to rape, and anger to murder; veering between overindulgence and the languid droop of stupefied indifference, sated beyond stir or concern.

This Enoch! Had he been the first of men, rather than Adam, there might have been no exodus from Eden! And it is strange and a bewilderment. Within the seed of Adam, was not Enoch already there? As well as Cain? Diverse, yes: but who is not his own ancestor? And why, after so many filters, life upon life upon life, why should Enoch be the only one to recall the fall of Adam? Keeping alive the guilt and becoming a fool in his own world, in terror of sinning.

Unbeknown to those who shared space on earth with him, a saint had entered their midst. That he had caused a stir in heaven and commotion in Sheol was not even known to his contemporaries. While the forces of Satan were alerting themselves and asking "This one? The Messiah?" his own father, Jared, was pitying his 'idiot' son, always in his depth like a dreamer, one moment stumbling with his head in the sky, the next, walking on the tips of his feet not to bend the grass. One night Jared had found him in the fields, his head on a stone, marveling at every star.

"Harmless," Jared reassured the ones who asked, until they all stopped wondering.

They passed him by now, caring little that he trembled with reverence, scarcely daring to breathe for fear of disrupting the invisible. They shook their heads when they saw him stroking the wing of a fallen bird for days on end until it healed and could fly. What they didn't know: the bird had made its report to God.

Thus, did his Father find him: gentle, frightened by sin. "Had you asked, I would have forgiven you," his Father spoke to his ear; then, He took Enoch by the hand and walked with him.

Enoch kept his eyes on the bird fluttering over them, the one he had healed. Then, gently stroking him, God took Enoch to His own bosom, that he might not fall and break a wing. For once, God intervened, cutting short the years of Enoch: three hundred and sixty five, in all, the solar perfection.

And God gave heed to Enoch's plea: find a way to redeem all men, beginning with Adam, and after. And it pleased God that the earth could host such sanctity, that man might open his heart to purity.

And God was patient.

Part 3
IT'S ... IT'S RAINING!

After God had cancelled death on behalf of Enoch, the earth was poorer. In protecting Enoch from sin, there had not been time for Enoch to have fully placed his seal of purity behind, that those who followed might have a beacon for inspiration. On earth, it might have been that Enoch had not lived; but for his son, Methusaleh.

This was seed that gave tribute to its donor; ripening through the nine hundred and sixty-nine years that was the life of Methusaleh, sending forth shoots to that other Lamech; and his was the seed that formed a canopy of clouds, announced by long trumpets, out of which the halo of Enoch descended gently over the head of the child Noah. It had already been determined by God that, henceforth, due to the growing poverty of men's souls, and the need for a light to guide them; henceforth, each saint would be given the fullness of all their years; that their joys might become flames engulfing sin; that their sufferings might intercede for the newly-awakened and the penitent.

The world that nodded silent greeting to Noah was fully structured already in patterned ways beyond the ken and outside the vision of Adam and Eve. In fact, under the shifting sands, and each new century's layer of rubble, the road back to Eden was lost to sight and, consequently, to mind.

As the air grew thin with increasing time; with memory more dilute; the very history of their first ancestors became less credible; more relevant to the unsophisticated. The recital of 'the Fall' which, at first, had been told in hushed whispers to reverent listeners over family fires now was reserved as an 'entertainment' for credulous children. Thus, awe gave way to reason; reason retreated before laughter; history became legend. Legend took hold of the imagination; and the imagination aimed at diversion; and diversion was, for its own sake, sifted from truth.

The man Noah lived in a world whose theme was deed, not mystery. His contemporaries were keysmiths who had already unlocked numerous secrets of nature, and now were running free without pause: absorbing, plundering, dominating the earth and sitting astride the oceans. Ingenuity and invention kept opening up new horizons, all the fervor of faith went into the rise of a new Eden where man would dominate over his own destinies. What had been wonder before became passion, as new victory laid open the earth to rape.

... But Noah's eyes were open and he saw the Infinity above the furies; and he wept in his heart that in every family, God was dead. When he had seen with his own eyes that even Death was scorned, and that not one could see through their own decay, he grew fearful and in the night, told God his anguish. Silence.

Now the days of man were grown shorter, even as the shadows lengthened over his sinfulness. The multi-colored bloom was gone from the desert; and it was a sign to the one who could see, and the eye was Noah's, that what had been nobly balanced in the struggle to survive was now degraded by excessiveness. And while man was in bondage to his senses, the breath of God was disgraced. The rivers were rising like swollen veins and the sun was in its dotage. The winds went searching, and there was white foam on the cold seas. Over all of this, the spirit of God hovered. Shame had given way to rage.

What was this work of deviant sense and aberrant device that it consumed the entire devotion and labor of one hundred and twenty years? So far, this was beyond comparison or counterpart in the human scheme. This curious bind of gopher-wood shaped like an ark for the oceans, yet resting elevated on a hill above the land?!

The builder, son of Lamech, called it 'a cry for repentance.' His cry carried over the heads of those below who labored their passion, and when they did look up and see what reflected the rays of the sun by day and was the cynosure of the moon's eye, they surely could not ignore it the same way they would turn from a mad dog or the soft-headed and insane among them. Those close to the family of Noah were more restrained, even attempting an apology for this work of art, this 'misbegotten monument.'

The legion of Noah's detractors, however, became insatiable in their tirades and scornful mouthings; sown by his dire prophecies and exhortations. In the early years, Noah had enjoyed some slight vogue, mainly among the bored and superstitious. Add to his audience a natural sprinkling of those cautious souls who take both sides, not to be excluded from the side of truth and there you have it!

As years passed upon years, Noah lost status and became an object of public curiosity and amusement. Whatever small reservoir of doubt Noah had drawn upon to gain a hearing was now exhausted; and by this time, the splash of crowds was a tired dribble. He was set upon by the mockery of children who were never children, taunting him with his own appeal, 'Repent and beware! Repent and beware!'

Yet, as one generation gave way to another and new children were now the sons and daughters of the first ones, Noah's faith never wavered. Except for short breaks when he seemed to be receiving mysterious instructions, Noah labored so constantly that his hammer seemed permanently joined to one arm, his saw to the other. There were these endless planks of gopher-wood, seemingly joined to infinity.

The years kept mounting and there was neither sign nor symbol to reassure Noah, only that Voice ... and it was enough. He was past his young manhood and his sons had taken wives who joined with them in the family shame, whispering among themselves.

In its one-hundredth year, the Ark had begun to emerge as an identity in the sky. Those who had ignored it for so long were now drawn to gaze on it, forced as it was upon their sight. Now there was a nervous edge to their laughter at the sound of the hammer and the scrape of the saw and Noah singing as he worked within sight of the Ark, which to Noah, was a holy temple. He knew God's time had come, and he prayed.

Then there was that day when among the idlers who stood about watching the Ark take on form there came a stranger, who was not a stranger, whom everybody knew, and nobody recognized.

Noah was at the point of bending a curve in the bow, a difficult feat, requiring the strength of more than one man, and he was sweating and straining to gain leverage under the braced fore-end. Without being asked, the stranger came forward and bent his shoulder behind Noah's. The plank broke in splintered halves, the first time this had happened to the pliant wood.

The stranger laughed, facing Noah's consternation as he turned around to see who had done this. "Thus, the Ark!" he whispered in Noah's ear. And Noah drew away from him.

"This, then, is the holy man, Noah. Pure lineage from Seth."

Noah could not conceal his repugnance. The stranger's face was a wart to his eyes, covered over with loose strands of hair. "I do not know thee," he said, finally turning his back on the darting, mouse-like eyes. Somehow, the desire came upon him to wash his hands and bathe his head in cool water. "I do not know thee," Noah reiterated. "Thou art not of man, nor beast, nor angel…. Thou are not of God, and I will have no truck with thee."

"Me, you have known, and will know again" The stranger's voice was soft, yet firm and grating. "I know, even as you know, that the waters will run with blood and there will be more waters, and the blood will be erased, becoming spittle on the foam, For as you were all spat out, so the phlegm is drawn in again and swallowed. All but thee and thine, Noah!" The beginning of a laugh, cut off without humor. "And I!"

The skin hung cold over Noah, and he felt prickles of fear over all his body. He bethought himself of prayer; but there was this voice again to which he must listen with fascinated horror. "And what happens when the rains are over; and the spill re-enters the soil unto its core? And you are left with this cargo of seed, beast and human; waiting to be fertilized, again to spout their natural infirmities." A long, terrible, curdling laugh that entered Noah's bones, and frightened off the spectators, who could not credit their senses.

"Remember me, those long nights at sea! Better yet, remember them! The forms and faces of all your neighbors! Don't mourn! Forget that you saw them drown! You'll see them again as they were. They will return to you as your children's children … and the world will not have changed!"

Noah worked no more that day. The stranger had departed as easily as he arrived. Somehow, though, whatever he had touched, even to the air that carried his voice, was profaned.

Noah's wife had that kind of worldly wisdom whose sharpness plumbs the roots but forever is surprised by the flower. While his sons only snickered through their fingers out of his sight; his wife took her prerogatives to the full; brimming over with sly aspersions, making a charade of studying the sky and commenting with assumed innocence: "Dear me, it hasn't rained since Father Lamech died... "

At such times, even Noah laughed. The years went by, and Noah saw that his wife had become crotchety and quicker to impatience. And he was gentle with her, even tolerant of her more pointed barbs. When he saw her, hands on her hips, staring at the Ark in the blaze of the sun, he knew from the set of her tight lips that she questioned his sanity. Her long protracted silences were become more meaningful, more challenging.

The day that she looked up to see the just-completed Ark perched high on the dry land; and Noah beside it, in the blinding light of the sun, pleased with his labor; that day, she burst.

"I know it!" she told herself, growing more agitated by the moment, "I know it! He's going to start another Ark!" She ran up the hill, confronting him, "I mean it now, Noah! If you were a mere hundred years old, I'd apologize for you, give him time. He'll learn! But Noah! You're nearly six hundred years old! Old enough to know better. Where is this rain? Was it God or Satan talking to you? Tell me!"

Noah scratched his head; then replied laconically, "I've talked to both and know the difference ... "

"You think! How many times have I watched you making noises to an empty sky! And you—only you!—see God in heaven. Why you, not me, not any of the dozen holy men I know! Don't embarrass yourself with an answer! I know that you're addled enough to listen to your own mirror!

"If it were only a waste of all those valuable years, it would be tragedy enough. But the blasphemy! To believe seriously that He who knows all would spend His time building up this great and beautiful world ... just to pass water over it!

"What a picture! How does your mind design it! The sea is floating with the bodies of the whole human race: watch out! Here comes the captain of the Ark. Here comes Noah waving his hat at the sky! Because you've seen fit to retire from the rest of us doesn't make you better than the rest; except that you indulge yourself, while we participate ... take chances with life as it is. What else?

"Imagine that! Seeing God as a petulant child overturning his building blocks! Alright, already! We all have our own private ravings and crazy fantasies. Yours created a shortage of gopher-wood! But must it be three decks high and over a hundred years long? And, I believe you're considering another one!

"Then to top it all, he's become a zoo keeper! Suddenly, before my astonished eyes, all the beasts, two by two, and all the things that fill the sky, two by two and all the creeping, slithering things from under the ground, two by two, filthy, dangerous things; yowling, growling, bundling into this one Ark. At least, you might have kept it private, a home for us. But, no!

"Who's going to feed them? Have you thought of that? When they eat what we've brought aboard, and it's gone, they'll eat us!

"While I'm at it, let me ask, give me to understand how the whole world could be corrupt; and only you, my saint, my patriarch, could escape untainted. Doesn't that sound kind of familiar to you? Like some of the madmen we put away?

"Once, I felt protected and safe; once upon a time your father brought you to my father, and you took me to mother your sons. Today, our neighbors feel safe to take the fruit off our trees, steal our sheep, change our boundary lines!

"For once, Noah, think of your own family! Look up and see how the lowest of the low laugh at me through you. Listen to me! Stop hammering for a moment! Noah! Noah! What's that strange look in your eye? Look at me, not at the sky! There's nobody there! I'm here. I'm talking to you. Who are you talking to, Oh, God, help me! Who are you talking to? What terrible things are you saying?

"It's getting dark. The thunder I hear the thunder! I'm afraid ...AFRAID! Talk to me Noah! The sky is getting darker ... Noah, Noah, Noah, it's ... it's raining!"

Part 4

THE TINIEST SPECK IN THE UNIVERSE

Spattering knives of water, burrowing, and piercing through the imprisoning soil; weakening the barrier until, with a mighty spring, the seal between the oceans was broken; and from opened lips, the under seas converged on the upper waves; shoulder by shoulder, undulating, leaping up, licking the frantic clouds; now scurrying, now dancing wild in the tempest of threat-realized skies, overfilled sponges.

The sun drowned.

The moon, in league with all the stars, shimmered on loose strands, a mobile in the wind, then, shivering out of orbit, one by one, like snuffed candles, the stars spattered out, engulfed, swallowed, gone; while the moon was halved, and quartered, refracted in a broken mirror before dissolving in the maw of dark waters.

Somewhere, hanging above the open pores; somewhere, stark against the last horizon; the last boat and the last survivor protested. The bow pointed up, end on end, dancing grotesquely on the tip and tongue of a giant wave. One arm reached up to keep the sky from falling but the fire-scarred and steaming billows bulged down joining seams to the waves and in the cradle of the trough still defiant, the arm was lost ... no, it rose again! The future, heroically futile against the new cascade of solid rain ... and there were no more tears to add to the flood. What remained, was the tiniest speck in the universe. Had there been time to measure emptiness, it would have been one hundred days past uncreation.

The anonymous gardens of oblivion, with arms folded, dared any impertinence from memory. The winds had found their caves; the waves, their depth; and the soft and luminous glow that was the Spirit, spent of anger; released from what had been yesterday, was exquisite with tranquility.

The COMMAND had returned whence it came. Yet, it was not

as if the Word had not been spoken! Infinity searched the finite for the fingerprint of creation, and there it was, the tiniest speck in the universe.

And, the darkness laughed at itself; and made way for a shaft of light which was the eye of God. And He dwelt on the Ark and on its cargo of more than ashes; and He was with Noah and his seed; and as time returned gloriously, the intermission between creations was ended.

Part 5

SANCTUARY

"Dry to the marrow! That's what you are! A ghost of a ghost. A naked will without flesh or skeleton. Pretending to sleep! Hiding behind a carpenter! I saw the lightening bring you here, then, you sat on the thunder to keep it quiet, to disguise yourself!

"Here it is, five days to the end, and you kept stretching, stretching, stretching these days like a sheet pulled flat at the corners, uneventfully. "If this were a garden, the weeds would have choked it all. The fruit is on the ground, brown and wrinkled and rotting, like in Eden. Here, at least, in the desert, the soil is stubborn to the seed. I expect no more and await the unveiling, I know! I know!

"You'll open your eyes; see the night still in the sky; stare at me like a good child that doesn't complain; and gather yourself together for a long babble of private mutterings that you call prayer, ignoring me like a dog; and you, the other dog with a bone that you won't share!"

This was not just another prod, another thrust in the middle of the night. This was no longer Satan the jovial guest at the wedding, waiting for the ceremony to end that he might share his gift. Of course, Jesus had witnessed the irritant, beneath the jocularity, that must scratch when it itches. But on this night, Jesus was resigned to the lost hours of rest; aware that the spur was now to Satan. There were fewer days remaining and the quiet pressures must build up steam—exploding bubbles of it—if there were to be any motion. Jesus realized as well as Satan that nothing short of capitulation or a total humiliation could salvage the pride Satan had invested here. Forty days, and 'no-contest' must be a defeat for Satan.

"In the garden of the Lord, the soil is the seed, the seed is the fruit, and the fruit is eternity. This, you must know," Jesus said, responding to the first challenge of Satan. "What went foul is now in Sheol," he added quietly.

And Jesus turned his back to Satan, that he might open his heart to the day. First, he must praise the Lord and expose himself to His will.

"Must you turn your backside my way!" Satan shrieked.

Jesus remained in his self-made sanctuary despite the malevolent heat of Satan's eye on his back, flaming with hatred. If he were not secure in the comfort of prayer, he would have taken more alarm at the edge to which Satan's temper had come. But he felt himself in the hands of God and nothing could violate that confidence.

"Pray! Pray for help!" Satan was hissing. "Too late! The props will collapse! All the pillars that hold up the universe will give way at once! The prisoners will be marched out for their last chorus. There will be a roar from all the assembled orchestras, shattering and splintering the main stage. The first major explosion will come from the Great Tempter and, knowing His penchant for the symbolic; this will signal the most spectacular of the conflagrations, and the graveyard will be Eden! The rest follows decrescendo. Creation is down to its lowest register, piece by piece flaring out, becoming ice, melting without mist. Thus, the last remaining lights, the stars fluttering down like dead leaves and, like fireflies without wings, the twilight of the falling angels ... and, at last, Perfection ... perfect silence."

Satan had expended the overflow of anger within this realm. Jesus rose from his knees, ending his prayers with a peaceful glance toward Satan. The maledictions had gone by him like a nightmare that has lost its fright because the faces under mask of darkness are all too familiar. Satan is never original, nor is negation a point of view. This canvas was an overpaint, beneath which Jesus recognized God's Last Judgement. The fear and terror that Satan had hidden was preempted and multiplied by the violence of his fantasies and the double coats of distortion.

Satan was breathing hard now, desperate for some sign, for any opening that would narrow the two-sword-lengths separateness so blood could be drawn. Yet, whenever the thought came—Lunge!—his footing was inevitably off balance, his palms wet and slippery.

Satan's eyes narrowed; concentrated slits of white-hot flame. There was a long bridge without breath, at the end of which Satan saw what had been happening. This was not the same Jesus! Day by day in the desert, so steadily that to one ever present the change would be imperceptible, Jesus was being transformed.

It was incredible to Satan, now that he thought back the thirty odd days since the arrival in the wilderness. What was gone in the flesh had grown in the soul, assuming formidable strength, an untouchability which only now was becoming visible. Yet, that did not begin to describe it. An answered prayer? The mission had found its leader? No, even more. It was as if, in the meanwhile, Jesus had gained a congregation; a whole family of men and women, waiting to be called. More than before, Satan was convinced that he had been brought into the presence of the Messiah.

But there was always that uncertainty! Satan gazed at Jesus, concentrating his focus and fixing his mind on the image, as if it might disappear, flutter away like a butterfly through a wide net; or become a mirage: the other side of his own reflection; that which men call conscience. "Satan with a conscience!" he exclaimed to himself, chuckling. Yes, there was Jesus, real enough, looking up cautiously at the sound of Satan's amusement.

"Butterfly did I say?" Satan enlarged on his musings. "More like a gray moth!"

Now that his suspicions were alerted, Satan's thoughts spread out like tributaries to a moving stream. However, every branch ended in the same sea. Who would follow such a guide, Satan asked, and answered, himself. Only the ones with nothing to lose: the disinherited, the underneath ones, needing a dream. Who else could swallow so strong a brew? Pure and naked spirit. The elite would never go for this! Otherworldliness is for the dying, the excommunicated poor, the ones without hope or pity for themselves...

" ... and their eyes, their ears, close as readily as they open!" Satan shouted aloud, triumphantly.

Jesus looked up startled, unaware of what had delighted Satan so grossly. Satan picked up the puzzled look and, keeping his voice raised, he flung the question at Jesus: "Will the dust of the cities, and the dregs of misfortune serve you better than these sand castles in the desert? When the Potter has failed, and the clay lies broken at

His feet, try putting it together: will it ever hold water?"

Now Jesus understood where Satan's thoughts were, and he replied firmly, "Clear water, yes! Where the silt and the sediment have settled their depths and been left behind. Can He who gave breath to the clay not fill His vessels with wine!"

"In which world?" Satan was become pugnacious. "Not the one I see! Some more, some, less. So what! I still say: every gust gathers its dust."

Jesus listened deeply; taking to heart every word Satan spoke. No lie must go unanswered. Soon he would be back among men again, and he would have to confront all of it, even that which posed as a friend to God. In these last few moments, he had become aware of a new strength an inner intensity in which fast and prayer had come together in a new harmony. That which had not been of the darkness was now all of the light. He was being called by name and the voice was the One who had first pronounced 'Adam.' Jesus knew then what it was to have had the first confidence of God, wander as you will, but do no sin.

To the extent of the fullness of his blessing, Jesus raised his head and nodded again and again, before sinking to his knees; then lying, flat-outspread, on the earth.

Satan looked at this with uncertain amusement. "How do you crucify the earth!" Then, probing the image to its ultimate ghost, he added, "Let his people eat him up!"

CHAPTER EIGHT
THE RAVEN FOLLOWS THE DOVE

"And you, Jesus.

Will you turn around and save yourself?

I doubt it.

Your life is already purchased.

Your destiny is wherever men congregate.

You, the dove.

I, the raven."

—Satan

Part 1

THE RAINBOW

The dove returned, dropping the tender branch at Noah's feet, and Noah lifted it reverently so that all might see. As they watched, struck by awe at this piece of their new world, the branch quivered between Noah's fingers; stirring, pulsing, sending forth its sap; uncurling a new green leaf on a twig that promised olives.

There had been many entrances to the Ark, taking departure from the corners of the earth. Now, there was only one exit and a destination whose baptism was toward a new life.

When the seas had settled into confinement and those on board were able to release their sucked-in breath without tension; when they had dried their glistening eyes and were able to laugh again, to their surprise, there was no hustle and bustle to the gangway. Instead, they were suddenly become modest and withdrawn; like children, loath to leave the familiar for the incalculable.

The moment was also strange for Noah. He found himself hesitating before giving permission to debark. This would be the last act of his command. Cargo, safe. Ship, delivered. Anchor, at rest. Port, closed.

If God had taken his hand this very moment and walked with him back to Heaven, his soul's journey would have been near-perfectly fulfilled. As it was, his will was no longer under guidance. And Noah foresaw a new world rising, with the Ark out of focus.

Moreover, with other and different choices waiting to be made in this new and unfamiliar precedence of values, there was all the jeopardy implicit in freedom, including the responsibility for sin. Noah trembled. He could hear the shrill voice of his wife, nudging him to give the signal. They were all looking at him now, waiting. But Noah remained at that last moment, looking over the Ark and fondly recalling all the years of his labors back to the glory of the moment of his annunciation.

The animals were now adding their impatient sounds and Noah sighed, but still could not let go, feeling an impropriety, needing more ceremony. He knelt and kissed the gopher-wood that had held off the assault of the waters; and as he knelt, he recognized what was lacking. And he bade everyone to come to their knees, and the Ark became a temple, as Noah raised his voice to praise God, "We give thanks to Thee, oh Lord that our lives were kept sacred; that we were spared the justice of Thy wrath; and given to know Thy love instead. May we be worthy."

Noah gave the signal now. The great parade out of the Ark began slowly and solemnly. They were on the peak of Mount Ararat and it was given to the redeemed that they would see the length and breath of the new world. Not immediately. At first, below their feet and beyond the mountain's edge, the vast plains of wet and hungry soil were still steaming in the brilliant light of the sun. The air was so dense with moisture and thick fogs in the valley that their first glimpse was of opalescent strands where the sun's rays were forcing an opening.

They were all of them now, man and beast, standing quietly in orderly file on the edge, eyes straining to where the clouds were grown thin to the last layers and the wisps were in motion. It was nothing: then, there it was—dear brother earth, so washed and clean and newly laundered. Come! Come! It seemed to be inviting all of them to take their chance on all its parts. Be fruitful. Multiply. Teem over the earth and be lord of it!

One of the sons of Noah, seeing a corner of the land he wanted to make his own, started down the mountain ahead of the rest. The melee began, a shrieking race in which no one knew his brother's name. Noah, watching, began to tear at his hair.

This time, the thunder was enough; bass voice ricocheting from the stone hollows. They paused, and looked back at Noah who had turned away from them. They returned, hanging their heads in shame, and frightened. "Lead us, father," they said with one voice.

Without a word, Noah led them back to the Ark. As they stood on its ground, he covered his head, and bade the rest to do likewise, "For this is holy ground," he instructed them. "We pray that the rise and fall of the waters has washed away and redeemed Adam's flaw in us. Henceforth, in the heat of our blood, we will be true to Thee. We grant to Thee obedience to Thy will; reverence to the Divine Name; and in the sight of this Ark, we swear forbearance from the worship of idols; nor will we indulge our flesh in what is abhorrent to Thee; neither incest, nor murder, or theft will have place before Thee and we shall abstain from the blood of the living beast."

Having said this, Noah opened his eyes, looking toward the sky. At the point of the tallest spire of the Ark, he saw a spray of blood-redness arching from one horizon to the other. Beside it, it seemed as if the fires of the sun had blazed and boiled over a whole cauldron of colors; a shimmer of iridescent dust from behind the utmost skies entered the palette; then, the deepest green that lay hidden in the soil awaiting fertility, added its warmth and texture. Behold! God has set His bow as an arch across the heavens. And within the secret places of their hearts, they could hear His voice, THERE SHALL BE NO FLOOD TO DESTROY THE EARTH AGAIN.

When the music of that silence was over, all the pairs of living things began their descent into the valley, home-seeking, searching out their true level. For a moment, there had been a pause in the cycle of the earth; spinning, hushed; all eyes caught up God's promise, all merging in the common breath; intake in wonder; expiration, a litany of prayer.

And since the days of the week had been lost with time in the duration of the flood; Noah called that day the Sabbath, worthy of God.

Part 2
DECRESCENDO

"The fishes survived the flood!" Noah's wife descended on him with great excitement, shaking him out of his afternoon nap.

Noah scarcely stirred. "Perhaps," he muttered in his beard, "perhaps the trout was as virtuous than the lamb." He waved her away, quickly dozing off again.

The earth hung steaming in the sky, drying out. It would be many a year before the soil lost its sogginess, and the molds ceased sporing in the ooze. Each time the sun rose and each time it set, the family of Noah would congregate ceremoniously; watching in silence as they remembered the dark days. At those times, the wait for the rainbow was the beginning of a sigh; expiring in tranquility as they remembered their good fortune.

The first days after the Ark were preoccupied with land, food and shelter. They found that the lush soil was well prepared for their needs; in fact, more than generous. Hustling in the common welfare, side by side, with unquenchable enthusiasm; they were soon rewarded by the first green stirrings in the earth. Even more, their first campsite had become a small village, with smoke rising and the sound of children's laughter.

The first commune had begun to give way to individual families seeking their own personal welfare. This transition had begun quietly enough in unequal prosperity when 'to lend and to borrow' supplanted the parceled shares. Only Noah's daily needs were set apart from this arrangement: it was not a matter of dispute that he was their leader whose labor had been the Ark, the instrument of their salvation.

With an ease reminiscent of Eden, the problems of survival were overcome without too much toil and sweat; and the days settled in with regularity. But now, time had begun to lag and grow drab. Noah had docked his ship, and his ambition went no further. His sons looked toward new horizons.

There were nights when they stayed awake with their memories, each one, secretly bringing to mind all the hustle and bustle of the vanished cities; longing in the depths of their hearts for the market-places with their excitement and iridescent splashes of hot colors.

What was most oppressive were the long periods of silence; the compacted stillness of a circumscribed world where all participants had had their say over and again and had been together too long in close quarters. How delicious was the recall of raucous shouts, the laughter and the endless parade of strange faces bending toward adventure!

How quiet the music!

Loosely, without commitment or even a spoken request, they began forming groups again; mostly, after the evening meal and before the onset of full darkness. If it needed an excuse, they would discuss the small problems of the day and exchange timid views. Noah took no role in all this; preferring to lean back and watch with half-open eyes.

Naturally, the discussions brought about planning and, just as naturally, several among them called upon their own past experience as a guide. Of course, one or another of their former friends and acquaintances would come up in conversation, either as a source of authority, or when the mention of one name would evoke another, then another; until quite innocently, and not intending to, each one gave up their secret return to memory, and exchanged portraits with growing enthusiasm and excitement.

More and more frequently, these gossip sessions became a rage; and soon it was as if their total involvement was only with the past, and it seemed so alluring in retrospect, except for the very last moment—this they did not think about.

The idea of the Flood became an isolated event with no point of contact to the world gone by, no more than a boundary line between two existences. Whatever else was brought to harbor on the Ark, that selfsame cargo of vain and pointless speculation disem-barked: old roots on new soil. Satan had foreseen the fall of moon-light on black leaves: greed and vanity. Was not Adam's seed on board?! Before long, lust would assume its flair and sin, its inventiveness.

But there was still the rainbow! And yesterday was yet the last day of the old world, so they took heed of Noah's croaking, "Repent and beware!" And they hid themselves from the past; and their terror brought peace back inside their nests.

This that was leashed by day was freed by night; and their dreams were taken up by the faces of the drowned floating out toward their inner eyes; staring, jealous of their comfort, begging in terrible voices, "Leave us to finish out our unfinished lives... "

And the sons of Noah belabored him with their dreams, asking for respite, only to learn, aghast, that he had had the same fill of the night. Every one of them was under siege, their dreams were spilling over with tortured souls begging for rest. Noah's wife was the most pitiful of all. She was not to be unconvinced that the Ark had really landed in Sheol; and her sanity was in jeopardy.

"A fine trick!" she shrieked in Noah's ear. "Where is salvation now?" she demanded, insisting that he make complaint to God.

Noah was reticent, even frightened and ashamed, to pursue God with this. His despair impinged on his faith; convinced as he was that it was he who had lost command. More reasonably, he assumed that with the Flood, there had been an overflow of dead spirits in Sheol; hence, this invasion.

It was time to consult God. That same night, as soon as the voices of the drowned began their lament, Noah covered his head and went outside into the mystic night. There were dark fires in the sky, and the star-points prickled his flesh. "My Lord," he whispered with reverence.

Silence rolled waves back from the closed sky.

Noah waited in quiet desperation, to his own shame dwelling on the many prayers he had not said, the more frequent lapses of gratitude and the thought that he had indulged himself in sloth and neglect of his hallowed new soil.

"My own children have been without an Elder," he grieved within himself. "and, I, too am bereft."

Noah refused to leave. He bent his thought toward the rainbow, gently chiding God for His disfavor. The night grew heavy; yet Noah remained, refusing to stir, hungering for ecstasy.

Worn down at last, the deep purple folds overhead rustled and quivered. It was not God, but the spirit of Adam that became visible to Noah. He looked through his memories and found Adam in all of them; and he was no longer filled with fear and frenzy, and the quiet returned to his spirit. "Father," like a child on his lap, he spoke softly to him, "help me to find peace."

"That is why I have come," Adam told Noah. "Thou, son of my son, " the voice cradled him. "Go, on your knees, go, Noah. Bend thy head in the presence of the Most Holy. Now, let thy lips extol the words that magnify His Great Name. May the Lord lift up His countenance upon thee, and give thee peace. Now, repeat as I say it: *Yisgadal vay yiskadash shmai rabu.*"

Thus, the *Kaddish,* the words to solace the dead, were placed in Noah's mouth and he took them to his heart. Adam's blessing remained with him into the morning and the new words were lamentations for grace of his lips and when he opened the seal on his eyes, he witnessed the final exit of the dead, parading with dripping shrouds. The plea was in their stone eyes as they turned their gaze his way but it was not for Noah to address them, though they were his own kin. As they diminished in the distance, calling his name in sorrow and utter despair; he knew he must not tarry, but turn quickly away, only to perpetuate praise for the Lord in His mercy. Noah returned to the living.

When the day was up, Noah gathered all of the clans together and told them all that had befallen him in the night. Word by word, patiently he taught the *Kaddish* to all but the youngest, who should have no concern with death. And once they all were freed from the bondage of their nights, they were able to sing and dance and play once more; even to place out of their minds that the nightmares had ever occurred.

Once more it would seem that God had need for man. What had been created needed to create! The village became a metropolis. The children of former children had sons and daughters. The world had shed its first skin. New forms and shapes rose from the earth like teeth in empty sockets; not lacking in art and invention. Every problem found its own special tool and from the earliest light to the last moment of twilight, men were opening veins in the ground, and packing the loam for a new world. What had begun in an inspired moment was become compulsive: a frenzy of solutions.

More than anyone, Noah was at odds with all this pulsing industry. It was not that the ship-builder felt no joy and amazement at what was being accomplished; it was that the captain had lost charge of the destination.

There were many dull days in which he kept himself aloof in his tent, bemoaning the fact that God had no more reason to confide in him. He would sit bent over, staring at his idle fingers, gnarled and callused: withering stubs without leaves, fingers that had bent strongly around the handle of the axe to cut the first beams for the Ark. The apogee of life was behind him, the highest wave had bent over and was rolling shoreward. Who needs a ship's carpenter? One hundred and twenty years experience! Captain of a ship, perhaps? Navigator of the greatest storm the world has ever known?!

How the days did hang heavily on his years! The assault of the wind and rain had left a creak in his bones and his eyes were constantly running over. Also, where was the reason: for what inspired cause should he heave into the tempest again?

Irritated by his own self-indulgence, Noah broke off his midday nap with a determined effort to pass the time more fruitfully. It was already the second nap this day. Several mincing steps away, he stopped to admire a new vine that he had not noticed before. How could he have ignored it?! The vine had insinuated itself around the trunk of a young elm tree; using this support to flaunt a spectacular display of fruit clusters; globules of gold and purple spheres, bursting with juice.

Noah went no further that day. With the same motion that Adam had made when he wrested the fruit out of Eve's hand; he brought the swollen sacs between his teeth, releasing the already-fermented juices.

There was a blessing on this vine; a gift of grace; a reward for his later years. His delight in the fruit grew insatiable. He stuffed his mouth while he squeezed out the juices for the next batch into the palm of his hand. Meanwhile, the color came into his cheeks. He felt exultant, dancing and swaying around the elm; then bracing himself on wide-apart legs as he felt the earth leap up in small waves. Suddenly, it was important to know, more significant than any mystery, to find out: if the dove had brought the olive, had the raven brought the grape?

Part 3

THE WASH OF THE FLOOD

The flood was in the overflow of words from the mouth of Satan. "Why don't you build an Ark for *yourself,* Jesus? Right here in the desert! There may not be another flood, but shouldn't you save yourself from the rainbow?!"

"Take straw, take brick, take wood, ice and metal, take whatever it is that sucks through the ooze, binding and joining the resistant hollows. Stir the still fires! Make a loud noise! And escape!

"What have you to do with the commonplace, the inadequate? To proliferate sin only in the mid-range without peak or valley, neither vice nor virtue! Don't touch them, find others like yourself, waken them with trumpets in their ears! Command their imaginations! I say to you, Jesus hear my words, let it end on the breast of earth, cover up the mistakes not yet made. Leave the worms to starve. Let them blame God for not feeding them!

"I tell you to preach doom. This is the theme they know best. This they remember, when they remember Eden. Preach doom and the children will understand their fathers and their fathers will understand their father's fathers... all the way back to the first Father. Oh, Jesus! Put them out of their misery. Let it end with the best. If your dance needs a flourish, put only one of a kind on your Ark! SAVE YOURSELF!

"One could debate it with you. Some adjustment. Some watering down. Some revision. A pinch of inhibition. A dash of sublimation. Control. Restraint, in some form or other, if only to keep the extremes in line, put violence in a cage. Be brave, Jesus! Time has opened more than one beginning. Look at Noah!

"That pitiful, pitiful flood, Jesus! Now, you know why Satan can laugh and cry all at once. With one eye I saw it as a raving speck, the dust gone mad in the smallest corner of the universe, and I blinked. With the other eye, I saw that miserable ant rising and falling in the waves, steering toward a rainbow. And I marveled at his endurance and fretted over his gall, riding over the bodies of three generations; preening and posturing—ah, Noah! Noah! Noah! You were closer to the drowned than you were to Him. Adam's children, Noah!

"And you, Jesus. Now that you've seen the temper and jealous fury of your One and Only; perhaps, you'll admit you are safer in my hands. The One who can unleash so much destruction can destroy you with a whim: the higher you rise, the more closely He watches; and you best not stumble. Bear in mind, His power is above Him. He is held captive by His own creations. There is only one escape. God can commit suicide.

"Save yourself from His good graces, Jesus; for, I see that you are favored. Be neither for nor against; but build yourself an Ark and sail clear of this desert. Take the role of Messiah, if that suits you. Find your own private wilderness; and don't even think the words you have spoken. Forget the rainbow, if it doesn't flood, it'll be fire and brimstone. What's the difference? The grumbling has begun. I can hear it in the hollows.

"Stand clear of the vice-ridden, virtue-shriveled cities. That's where it will happen next. Look at this beautiful clear white sand, think of it as a nest; a ship of the desert for the next Noah.

"Can you read what the finger has traced in the sand? Have you seen the 'sign' in the parchment? There are those amongst us who think of the scripture as an extravagant canvas, stitched on piece by piece, trying to match the fading colors with bad replicas. To me, it is more than history. I track down the 'sign'; that sudden glow of 'divine desire' exposing the bones and sinews of conspiracy; and we know in Sheol where and how to defend ourselves. Why do you suppose I'm here? Those oversize inspirations; prophets barking like dogs in the night; the different breed, these are the flares of the armed camp; and our spies are ready, searching out the weaknesses; seeing where the belly is exposed.

"And humor! Can't you hear poor old Noah crying 'Repent' to his neighbors, how small was the Ark?! Suppose he had convinced one or two hundred of them; their wives and their children, what then?

"See what I mean? God never intended to save a soul of them!"

Part 4
EN PASSANT

"This is the Bible!" Satan held out a parched-skin covered tome; making no effort to conceal from Jesus' eyes that the hand-lettered vellum was full of erasures and recent insertions. "We believe in keeping old fruit fresh," Satan explained, advancing a response to the look of distaste on the face of Jesus.

Without further ado; squinting, winking, blinking; scratching his head at intervals, Satan began to read. His voice was a monotone, and he stopped between words, editing and polishing in advance, before speaking, and when his own censorship brought him to a full stop, he fumbled and apologized lamely, "The words are like insects that would scamper off the page if one didn't keep them tight-focused with squeezed eyes."

Then he started all over again, reading more facilely, "Thus, when the angry waters had washed away all traces of love, they receded and become a subterranean ebb. Once more, the world was what it had been before.

"Say that for the witness of Noah! Into the earth with him! May the blindness pass unto the generations! The eyes that have seen the flood are full of sand: who remains to give testimony? Who else, among men, has seen creation's stage swept clean? The sons and daughters of Noah banished from memory what their minds were loath to recall, and they dared not open their own children's eyes to that pitiless testament. So it was that their lips were sealed; and the children, immediate with their own concerns, were too preoccupied to ask questions or to wonder about what was past and long ago. So it was that the unanswered question that was never asked was never the burden of the children of their children, who *did* ask questions, but could get no reply. *Man is the one who remains the same. That which changes are the plans of God!*"

Satan never gave credit to the unknown patriarch of Sheol who had written that last comment in the margin but he savored the taste of it, enjoying the innuendo.

As for Jesus, he was already in the loom of the fortieth day; recognizing the singular edifice Satan had spawned for the real peril it was. His hope and trust were still in the inhaled breath of God that was in man. Satan saw the exhale, but Jesus held firm that the breath had entered the blood and reached the heart, where its essence was unassailable; not to be exhaled. The first night in the desert, within that first dream, he had spoken the words that were to become his legend, "Give me lips for the hearts of men!"

Now, watching the postures of Satan, Jesus tensed himself against his own natural charity and feelings of compassion for the fallen angel. This unnatural, this anti-God, was the enemy of creation. Ultimately, nobility lies within truth and truth is above mercy.

No part of the battle would be defaulted, Jesus decided; recognizing that the unoccupied field becomes Satan's province. And he answered Satan, "After the flood, when the world had become again the first image of God, as God had seen it," Jesus looked directly into those terrible, glowering eyes that opposed him, "once again, man was in the fullness of himself, joining loin to muscle and heart to spirit, in that labor that blesses creation. Man bit into the soil with his teeth, tearing out the worthless roots, preparing the loam for its wedding with the seed. Once again, he was the envy of the animals. And he found the earth open and waiting; a needless conquest. Once again, as it had been in Eden before, with grace and dignity as God had given it; freely granted in love to free men and women. Thus, the breath was honored."

At first impatient, Satan turned jocular, chanting with a lilt, "Did it pay I wonder, to fire the clay, and blunder into an overflood of clay turned mud, red and brown and watered blood? What behavior for a savior!"

Satan turned lugubrious, wiping his eyes with the back of his hand, satirizing the absence of feeling. He had seen the hardening of Jesus' resolve: his response was pure, uninhibited buffoonery, combining a peculiarity of sobs and laughter. Yet the somber plan was there. Suddenly, he shot out at Jesus, "How often should the

Master pick up his fallen puppet? Are you here to repair the strings, to bind the arms and legs together? You call this love! Your puppet falls before it rises . . ."

Satan spun his head around as if it were mounted on a turning circle. "I say that man falls because he rises! How can he compete with God?" Satan came out with it fully now, blazing with venom. "I say to all your Messiahs, when they come, if they come, suck out the breath! Be rid of this imitation of God! Become what it is, not the image of it! There it is: the goad! See that substance under the clay; the foreign breath itching the skin, raising welts, and emptying the lungs. There you have it: man is allergic to His breath!"

Satan was dancing with his theme, hopping from one leg to the other irrepressibly, growing red in the face. With one strange impulse, he leapt over Jesus' head, coming down slowly, reciting this ditty, "As I see my portals brim with mortals, I wonder, are they truly the breath of Him; or merely the image of His whim; *else I would be imprisoning Him!*"

Jesus looked up and saw the star now constant above his head. It had been rising higher each night, now, toward the end of the forty days it was almost at its zenith. With the joy of it came the pain, as the voices of suffering grew above a whisper in his ears, and he could make out the outcry of frightened children. He looked down at his hands, held out helplessly; and he felt the healing gift prickling the tips of his fingers. He raised his hands up high, that in being borne upward, they would be blessed by He that had called for the light and seen it come.

And Jesus made reply to Satan, "Wherever he is; whether from his bed of sin, within or without the gates of Sheol; I say to you that no man's neck is bent that low; nor is the sky so forever dark and far away that the burdened heart may not take communion with the Holy Spirit in covenant with God." Although what he was saying was meant to be no more than a profession of faith under the attack of Satan, the embrace of its meaning brought warm tears to his eyes, and Jesus fell to his knees in prayer, with Satan bending over him, shocked into silence.

That night, Jesus saw through the darkness, as from a deep cave into the night; and he learned that it was always there, not just following the storm, "The rainbow!" Jesus called it out with such fervor that it would seem to go beyond the sacred promise to Noah and his kin.

Satan was surprised. In his vision, the rainbow had always been in the sky. It had not occurred to him that most others were not aware of it. But who besides he would be threatened; fearing arrows from out that arch?

Part 5

HOW FAR DOWN IS UP?

"Why not?!"

"Why not build a tower? Let it rise up, and keep rising as high as it can go and then use the top as a bottom for another height. I can imagine looking down, each of us from his own star."

"Looking down?"

"Looking up! A circled road rising, ever-rising without end. Son beyond Father, where the floods can't reach!"

"Eden is there!"

"Why not?!"

"To fly without wings; to aspire beyond sight; awakening the sleeping light. To breach the outer reach; ever higher, unabated; Heaven, at last!"

"Why not?!"

"Are not all things possible to Man?"

"Why not!"

This once, perhaps never again, one singular, undeviating force lunged skyward; its purpose fixed by all of mankind simultaneously: everyone subjugating self to the common course. In this insanity, sanctioned by mutual agreement; the same look was in every eye, necks craned at the same angle, and the endless days shared one dream ... higher!

To what purpose was the perfect mechanism pride had wrought from desire? What lust had fused the separate cells, making one body of men with thousands of eyes; waves of left arms and legs synchronizing with waves of right arms and legs, a choreographic centipede.

An army of fingers shaped the bricks from mud; and the vast fields where the wheat had swayed in the wind now harvested bricks, baking and firming in the sun, from horizon to horizon. A conveyor belt of hands passed bricks, one to the other toward Babel.

Bond the brick with bitumen! More brick! More bitumen!

The first stairs upward! Nary a sound of thunder. The first platform to the stars. Celebration! Then a pause: fear, anxiety, timid
glances at one another: "It is for the greater glory of God!"

The theme, the rational: one chord became a symphonic outcry.
Pride had its pretext; as each new platform set a notch in the sky.
Now it was that the seed of Cain sprouted; passion took the lead,
with fury and frenzy keeping pace; and they assailed the heights feet
over head over feet, scorning the lowest.

The clouds threw shadows on their faces; there was no more joy
in their eyes. Even as the shade lengthened; the upper lights began
their own invasion, casting down blinding streaks, opening fire in
the eye back to its own skull.

Past the first barriers, the next thrusts upward became rapine,
coarsening the spirit, brutally exposing skin under skin, flesh under
flesh, stripped down right to the first ember of the flame burning in
memoriam of the divine spark. The last residue of awe and reverence
dissipated; that holy cenable where the image of God was kept, was
violated, assaulted by lewd outcries.

Just beneath the clouds, the one whose eager reach, stopping
short at nothing, had outdistanced the others; stood alone on the
platform with horns of mist; cupping his hands in the semblance of
a ram's horn: "Make way, God! Here we come!"

The echo bellowed back from a range of mountain peaks below;
and the insolence was thrust back on all who heard. A forest of eyes
looked upward in fear: this had been more than sin—rebellion!

For awhile, the silence indulged itself, anticipating the echo from
Heaven; ready to recant at the first roll of thunder; which never
came. Now the breath came out of restraint; unstrung tensions were
animal outcries; and all the way down the circular stairs, the regular
beat of clapping hands, reached the apex of delirium.

Having dispensed with God; they blessed their own labors; idol-
atrous toward accomplishment. They trespassed the lower heavens
by ingenious pulleys and lifting devices. Like spiders, they wove
strands from the clouds, crisscrossing cables from one platform to
the next higher; reaching, finally, where the stars could not hide.

Now it was that the melancholy eye of God bent below and mea-sured His patience, seeing to what worship man had succumbed. He sighed. And His infinite weariness was not buried in time; and the song of His sorrow was heard by all the rest of the universe.

"Eve! Where are you?"

"Adam! Where are you?"

The plaintive sound again! Punishing the memory, weeping in the wind, drooping the willows; raising the head of the serpent.

And God dreamed below His rainbow, forbearing the seed but not the deed; while, where he slept, the Messiah stirred. Yet, brick by brick continued the rise; ignoring the rush of voices in the wind, Adam, Enoch, Noah, warning them, trying to cool their blood; and he, who had been first to the clouds was given the voice of prophe-cy and he repented himself, crying from his soul: "Repent and beware! Go below! Cover your heads and worship!"

And they came upon him like beasts, believing him mad; nor could they endure his shining face, adoring his vision, "The song of the psalmist shimmers the harp; and I am one note, trembling in ecstasy!"

And when they had finished with mockery, they flung him into the void and found their eyes wandering toward the depths, follow-ing the spirals until their heads spun dizzily; their tongues curled up in the caves of their mouths and their ears were set to strange rhythms and stranger harmonies; inverting their speech so that the words wriggled and whirled, and fell to their feet like worms to be stepped on angrily.

In the confusion of strangers; the left limbs no longer recogniz-ing the right; losing unison, becoming creatures of anger, gibbering witlessly; kicking, scratching, biting, hopelessly inharmonious.

So, for many suns and moons, it rained bricks from on high.

CHAPTER NINE

"GREATER LOVE . . ."

Not a word to God; for is He not a God of truth
and justice and love? Would He ask of me what
shatters my soul? Let me out of pasture to die?
"Lord, I am unworthy! Silent be my lips."

Not a word to Sarah; she, who laughed at an
impossible joy; then, saw herself fulfilled. Better it
had never been than that the miracle retracts itself.

Not a word, not yet, to Isaac; looking ahead of his
joy still, believing the promise hammered, nail by
nail, star by star, into the sky.

God has asked of me, that for which my voice has
no breath. Let the 'yes' instead, breathe inside my
heart, unspoken.

Part 1
GENEALOGY

Sifting, sifting, sifting the spare earth; two years beyond the Flood; Shem, father of Arpachshad.

This wasn't the one!

Adam's relic within Noah's seed churned and fizzled and popped precociously, thirty-five years, and here's Shelah!

Not yet!

Shelah; Eber; Peleg; Reu; Serug; Nahor, not a grain of gold in all the sifted sands.

Patience.

Then, Nahor took from the womb, making room in the sun for the first of his name. Thus, in the land of Ur among the Chaldeans there toddled and walked and strode like a man a heathen among heathens bearing the name Terah.

Alas, he was not to be!

Yet, when he wed, the night of his nuptials, there was the clamor; joy in heaven at what was begotten. Once more, but quietly, the light entered the world, filling in the long darkness between dreams.

The eyes of the prophets were closed while the stars danced. The stone ears of the idols, side by side, heard nothing but that a baby cried, Terah sighed. The song in praise of creation that morning, midwife to the new life, a new dawning, and the day spread out its arms in longing.

Terah had reaped more than he sowed; nor was he impressed that God blessed his seed. Yes! Another star in the sky. Guess! How many, and why and why? The same scrape of the same plow on the abused soil. The true fallings of Adam's Clay: Seth, Enoch, Noah, Shem, now, this goal of flesh merged with the soul; God's breath against the angel of death.

Abram.

Even now, walking among men; questioning the indifference of those learned in the role of the stars. Yet, because of the confluence; henceforth, the palette of the spirit would have new minglings of color.

Abram.

Had there been this one star less, the fullness of love would have been impossible; death, unbearable; sacrifice, unknown and inconceivable. Let this star never have been, and who might hope for Heaven; would there be one to desire it? The very salt and savor of all our senses are in this; as well as the ways of daring and courage; the reach of the heart and the flight of the mind. Who has not called for help in the deepest pits of the darkest night, waited for an answer, and heard the wings of the messenger! Breathe! The air will enter your nostrils and fill your lungs. Of such is faith!

And faith is the grain of gold in the sifted sand. Faith is Abram!

Now they dream, even in Sheol.

Part 2

DUOLOGUE

Satan: Very well. Put Abram in the black. All this investment in Creation, then, wiping it out, and starting all over again, something had to pay off! Let's be kind and say that the adolescence of man has run its course. Granted! Now what about this forced and unspontaneous maturity? Say what you will about Abram: he is not exactly what you would call the fresh clay of Adam.

Jesus: And the words of God came to Abram: "Follow me," and Abram listened and did God's bidding. "Leave your country, your family, and your father's house, for the land I will show thee … "

Satan: Aha, the bribe again! God is out shopping for love! "I will make of you a great nation." If nothing else, the thunder is muted.

Jesus: And the man of God tasted the wine of his soul, and bowed his head in deep reverence. And the seeds of unborn generations waiting to be multiplied by the number of stars, waited on Abram's lips. And God heard the word as it formed in the heart of his servant, and was pleased by him.

Satan: Pleased!? Surprised! Overwhelmed would be more exact. One drop of faith for an ocean of bounty. How's that for a bargain? "Here, take this! Take that! Look all around you from where you are towards the north and south, the east and west, all the land within your sight, I will give to you and your descendants forever."

Jesus: Thus, in the first morning's dawn, Abram rose with the sun, and set forth toward destiny, destiny's name being Canaan. The words spoken by God were a serenade in his hearing; nor would he interrupt their melody with bread or sleep. At Hebron, he could not contain his joy, nor go further without some service toward gratitude. There in Hebron, he paused that he might raise an altar upward to commemorate the promises made by God. There, also, he prayed that he might be worthy of the seal.

Satan: Those were the days we bethought ourselves of Armageddon. The dead were streaming in their graves; and the night was in flight with feathers and claws, shrieking maws, and closing doors. But I turned my own eye on this one favored by God's grace, studied his way, then summoned all the princes: "Dust be still! Bonds, unjoined! This is not the Messiah!" How did I know, Jesus? This! See this! This is the eye that saw him at the Negeb when he deserted, leaving the sick and starving to their fate, to save himself from the Egyptians. That may be the way of a prophet, but who would imagine the Messiah saving his own skin?! Mind you, if you would learn about Satan, *when I seek the sign, I find the flaw!* Here! Here! Even more! I was there when Abram pandered the body of Sarai, his wife; to spare himself assault. Was God there, or did He turn His eye away while his servant Abram took Pharaoh's bribe of livestock, stuffing his robe with gold and silver coins? God was there, all right. If one must weep, weep for Pharaoh who was not made of stone, and punished for it in ignorance of Sarai's state. No, Jesus! Not this one! Even if Messiahs came in various sizes; and this, a smaller one, not this one! My other eye is on Abram now; haggling with his brother, Lot, already making parcels of the land granted him in perpetuity....Truthfully, Jesus, isn't the mask too big for the face inside? Isn't God stretching his need just a little?

Jesus: At the full harvest, there are always those who complain that the wind and the frost would level the soil again. They are the ones who do not see life rise from death, that they might worship. Have you not seen how loose is the touch of the pollen on the stamen; that it may let go, and take root?

Satan: That Abram gives off his parcel in Sodom to his brother, Lot, that news is good to me. Leave it at that. The time is for the sliver of a moon. Leave it for my prayers.

Part 3

HAGAR

The earth gave forth to Abram in lush profusion. In the ten years that had gone by in the land of Canaan, he had watched his flock multiply; the young crawling over each other. The many pestilential outbreaks that had ravaged and decimated other tribes nearby passed over his tents in quick winds, sparing them. Abram was loved, respected, a leader among the neighboring tribes; wealthy by any standards, and for this he was not envied.

The lack was in that immeasurable gain that enriches the bitter cup of the poor; that demeans the harvest by its absence; that takes the glitter off the gold; unsaltens the meat; and dries the oasis... Sarai was barren! What matter all the rest, if the seed remained unfructified; and the immortal chain from Adam was without a link...

Abram had talked with God, had he not? It was His voice that he heard speaking... making promises! The memory remained stubborn and as much as Abram pondered and racked his brain; the sift of every word left gold behind. Surely, the promise was there.

Sarai was more disconsolate; taking upon herself a sense of unworthiness, and the burden of failure. In the fullness of many a night, she would stare despondently at a pregnant sky abundant with stars; and all this sprawl of fecundity was, of itself, a mockery. So many harvests had come and gone and returned again; so many new heifers; and then those horrible awakening screams in the night, bringing someone else's son to birth in the morning... to another woman who would scarcely take heed of the new face for the many already at home.

How can there be descendants without children? Again, she asked it of herself; turning to look at Abram; wondering why he had not become more bitter; watching how soft and evenly he breathed; that his brow was serene. "Won't you remind God of his covenant?" she whispered in his ear, hoping it would pierce through his sleep. At the word covenant his lips parted in a soft smile; though he did not waken.

It was that same soft smile, so full of confidence, that brought her secret thoughts out of their hiding place. "The promise had been made to Abram. To his seed." She studied the silent sky, "It is *I* who am not worthy!"

It agitated her to confront what followed, that Abram might consent to put her aside, despite the love that she knew he truly felt for her. It was then that she bethought herself of her maidservant, Hagar. Providence had provided a more fertile soil.

That same morning, filled with bad grace, she sought out Hagar and bade that she cleanse herself thoroughly, and be purified as for a wedding. Nor did she mention the name of the groom. She gave Hagar her own white robe; and brought her within Abram's tent that he might study her and be pleased. Nor did the proud and pleased look in Hagar's eyes, opened by surprise, escape Sarai's glance.

Abram looked up when they entered, and saw that Hagar was nubile and comely, but his first concern was with Sarai; dejected and ready to cry.

Sarai lowered her gaze, and looked away; managing her words with great care: "It is right, if it is I that bring her to you," she spoke without joy. "Never forget it was I who brought her!"

She turned away, quickly closing the flap of the tent behind her.

Thenceforth, Hagar was relieved of all her former duties; and Sarai avoided the sight of her. When they met unavoidably, Sarai's way was unceremonious, directing her gaze on Hagar's waistline that there be no mistaking her tolerance, and the difference of caste.

In later months, when the evidence had become most clear; Hagar took privileges upon herself she would not have dared before; becoming haughty in Sarai's presence; even insolently indulging herself, indiscreetly entering Abram's tent when Sarai was present, flaunting her new position. And Sarai saw to her bitterness where the first seed had fallen; so that she withdrew further inside herself, mourning over her dead womb.

As the time for delivery approached nearer to hand; and the signs of growth, so quickly fulfilled; the sight of Hagar in Sarai's eyes became less endurable. The very bulk of her servant's waist distorted itself as another sign of her humiliation; and she could abide it not one more day. Sarai came before Abram weeping copiously to cover her rage and frustration, totally ignoring that it had been her own scheme to begin with: "May this insult to me come home to you! It was I who put my slave girl into your arms; but now, that she has conceived, I count for nothing in her eyes. Let God judge between us!"

Until that moment, Abram had not truly understood what had been churning inside Sarai. Now that she laid her misery at his feet; he came closer to her, and ran his fingers through her long silken hair with special care and tenderness. His eyes softened, and he spoke to comfort her: "Your slave girl is at your disposal. Treat her as you think fit," which was as much as to say: only you are the true wife of my flesh.

From that time onward, Abram kept his distance from Hagar; yet remaining gentle toward the needs of her time. It was Sarai, however, who kept seeking out Hagar; unloosening her rage, even striking her at times, so that Hagar began to fear for her unborn child.

Hagar had matured quickly, leaving behind her childish ways as her time drew closer. She grew in dignity and grace, even as the holy vessel itself is anointed before receiving the spirit. Now, all her hopes were with her son (for a son it would be, she knew). This son of her flesh would stand beside Abram; and he would be a Prince; the first and the rightful heir.

Hagar clutched the dream to her breast, and suckled it as if it were already born. She would try to be private with her joy within Sarai's gaze; keeping her lids half-closed, and looking off elsewhere.

One day, toward evening; as Hagar lay resting from the day's heat, rubbing her hands over her girth and singing softly to herself; Sarai came upon her; and the madness rose without restraint , accusing Hagar of sloth and self-indulgence. Hagar saw the threat of violence loosening its bonds; and, mindful of her precious burden, she fled into the night, expecting never to return.

Hagar was well on the road toward Shur when she saw that the way ahead was blocked. The face was another moon between the tops of the trees; and it spoke with the timbre of a lyre, revealing itself as a messenger from the Lord. *"Go back to your mistress and submit to her ..."*

What had Sarai confided to God? Hagar was not clear in her spirit; only certain that her son must survive. She backed off, resisting the impulse to rush past the open, restraining hands of the angel. Her hands protected her stomach and she could feel a windmill of kicks beginning inside. She stopped to listen; her face widening in smiles, smoothing out the lines of pain. The moment was not yet; but was this not *life* stirring within? Slow and careful, she eased herself down to the hard earth. The knots which had tensed her neck and shoulders undid themselves and Hagar bent over her womb, paying proud tribute to the throb and pulse whose rhythms were combining in currents with another tide, no more just her own.

"You will bear a son ..."

What was the angel saying, telling her what she knew already. Her mouth opened wide, and the dryness of her lips was not relieved by the hard point of her tongue.

Her eyes bulged, and she began to pant, while trying to hold back, telling herself, "Not this way! Not here!

"... and you shall name him Ishmael: which is to say, 'God has heard'."

God has heard! He will be a prince! Hagar turned her head upward, unpressing her knees where they had left white marks on each other. Not here! Ishmael! She half-rose, supporting herself on outstretched arms and half-bended knees, offering herself before the sky; swaying her body like a cradle. For that instant, she was joined to and became part of, that great glory wherein the first seed becomes new in the beginning of a new and powerful nation.

When it was over, that mysterious blessing; and the angel had discharged his message and gone; Hagar was able to move again, picking herself up carefully, and turning back out of the night to where the father might attend the birth of his own son.

Part 4
SODOM & GOMORRAH

Abraham sat at the entrance to his tent, his chin on his chest; dozing but not quite asleep. The sun had reached its height, casting few shadows so that when he half-opened his eyes he beheld at first a shining blur; then a radiance that caused him to blink, then shade his eyes. Was it one face or three that hovered over him?

Quickly, he gathered himself together and rose to his feet. He felt flustered by the sense of an important presence; paying scant heed to a murmured apology for disturbing his peace; responding instead to the strong urge he felt to make obeisance, that the strangers might feel properly welcomed.

He bowed to the ground, "My lord," he called up, though three figures seemed to be wavering and rippling in the heated air, "I beg you, if I find favor in your presence, kindly do not pass your servant by."

Now there were distinctly three! Three, as if in a dream! Abraham rubbed his eyes vigorously; yawned shortly, then clapped his hands together once to show he was now alert. He spoke briskly, "A little water shall be brought. You shall wash your feet and lie down under the tree. Let me fetch a little bread and you shall refresh yourselves before going further."

They replied in unison: "Do as you say."

Abraham paused for an instant, that voice, common to all three, was ancient in his memory.... Then he hastened inside the tent, scurrying, calling to Sarah with urgency, "Hurry! Make haste! We have guests! Knead three bushels of flour and make loaves."

In the midst of the bustle, a thought struck him; and he stopped to peer through the folds of the tent, neither horses or camels were in sight that might have belonged to the strangers. His heart throbbed at this new evidence; but he kept it to himself; now running out to choose a tender calf that the servants might prepare; and, while the strangers took their ease under a large shade tree,

Abraham set large pitchers of cream and milk before them, that they might enjoy his hospitality.

Nor did Abraham stop to reflect that he, a chief among chieftains, should go so far beyond the normal courtesies of welcoming travelers to become almost servile in his attentions until the guests smiled at him with favor. Only then did he sit down with them to break bread and take salt.

In their midst, it seemed to Abraham that their image was overly dazzling, more than could be explained by the brightness of the sun, and though there was one before him, one to the right and one to the left of him, yet he felt uncertain whether the three had been one; or the one had become three.

Still they spoke in one voice, asking: "And where might your wife Sarah be?"

They knew! Sarah—not Sarai! "She is in the tent," he replied simply.

Now the wonder corroborated itself: "*I shall visit you again next year without fail; and your wife will then have a son.*"

Were they speaking of another kind of conception!? Sarah, who had been hiding behind the entrance to the tent, listening attentively; covered her mouth but could not restrain the laughter over her cupped hands.

The sound came out like an embarrassment; and, suddenly, Sarah heard the voice that filled the tent: "Is anything too wonderful for God?"

The laughter froze at the root of her throat; and Sarah became fearful. Abraham replied for both of them: "My Lord has not come all this way to tell his servant what he has already taken to heart. Both Sarah and I await the ultimate blessing of our years and his name shall be Isaac. In what manner may I serve you now, my Lord?"

And having spoken the name, Isaac, Abraham recalled that once before, he too had laughed in his throat and now that Sarah echoed it, it came to him finally why the name had come along with the prophesy. *Isaac*: God has smiled. God has been kind.

His joy now left its prison, leaving behind the feeling that he had seen through the face of the sun; seen the shadow of a shadow's shadow which was three, which was one, which was His own holiness.

Now it was unmistakable and not a daydream; the Voice that took him into its confidence and it tore at Abraham under the last skin to be present before so much sorrow, *"How great an outcry there is against Sodom and Gomorrah! How grievous is their sin!"*

At this, Abraham screamed with terror and fell to the ground, covering his face. When he could speak, his lips trembled and he spoke with the lowest breath in his lungs at the bottom of his throat, for he dared the wrath of God, "Does the rainbow condone fire and brimstone?"

His reply came quickly: *"Will the Judge of the whole earth not administer justice?"*

Abraham breathed softly; but his heartbeat became more rapid, for he was now on hallowed ground, at the source of God's love. Somehow, yet without full certainty, he understood that God was pleased with him for interceding. God wanted salvation; some alternative for redeeming the children of Sodom and Gomorrah, even at this late hour! "Yet," Abraham asked himself, "what ransom would ring true? Are you ready to destroy the just man with the sinner?"

Having said so much so hastily; he repented himself, reading the silence that followed more as pain than anger. Yet even knowing that he knew imperfectly, Abraham saw in his conscience that he must continue his outcry, "Perhaps there are fifty just men in the town. Will you really overwhelm them, will you not spare the place for the fifty just men in it?" Then, filled with the horror of what impended, Abraham let his feelings overflow, "Do not think of doing such a thing; to kill the just man with the sinner, treating just and sinner alike! Do not think of it!"

And God looked at his servant with kindness, knowing what He knew, and pleased that Abraham was faithful to the living soul: *"If at Sodom I find fifty just men in the town, I will spare the whole place because of them."*

Grateful tears came into Abraham's eyes, and he spoke again: "I am bold indeed to speak like this to my Lord, I, who am dust and ashes. But perhaps the fifty just men lack five: will You destroy the whole city for five?"

His reply was soft-couched and patient. *"No, I will not destroy it if I find forty-five just men there."*

"Perhaps there will be only forty there."

"I will not do it for the sake of forty."

"I trust my Lord will not be angry, but give me leave to speak, perhaps there will be only thirty there?"

"Not for the sake of thirty."

"Twenty?"

"Not for the sake of twenty."

Abraham trusted hope further. "Ten?"

"Not for the sake of ten."

Beyond that, Abraham dared no more, rejoicing in his heart that he had been chosen to witness the immensity of God's mercy. Had he only known! If, beside Lot, there had been only one other just man in Sodom to plead their cause, that too would have turned away the wrath of God.

Part 5

FULFILLMENTS

There was a flare-up of fires on one side of the plain, celebrating the dawn. Directly across, on the darker side, Abraham saw huge columns of smoke rising out of the blazing furnace that had been the left and right hands of Satan on earth: Sodom and Gomorrah.

Satan watched and wept and railed against Heaven as never before. It is said, without witnesses, that Satan had dared the flame at its height, and made himself visible on the streets of Sodom without disguise. More than anything else, this preview of Satan's rage and frustration was the last sight, and the greatest fright of all for the screaming victims.

Abraham never stirred. His head was covered, and he was on his knees; his face reddened by the blasts of heat that rolled across the plain. When the last wisp of smoke had curled upward, Abraham wept quietly for the victims of the holocaust; for God, whose mercy had been brought to such tragic exhaustion, and for himself, who had sinned in taking joy at being spared.

Now, what had been the riotous life of the cities was leveled to dust and silence. *There had not been ten just men to plead for Sodom and Gomorrah.*

Almost, but not quite on the anniversary of the great conflagration, in the one-hundredth year of his life, God's promise was made known to Abraham. Isaac, he was called; and, above all the joy, it was God's laughter that was heard and heard again, eight days later when Isaac was brought in covenant with Himself.

Sarah was fulfilled. The late fruit was even sweeter to her taste. God's laughter had forgiven her own. Now, she could hold her head like the queen who was Abraham's wife. Isaac she guarded with a fierce devotion, getting up more than once each night just to adore the sight of her son and reassure herself that he was well and out of harm's way.

At the same time, the very sight of Ishmael offended her eye; knowing that he had a claim on Abraham. That the son of Hagar should be even in the presence of Isaac turned her toward rage and she treated the older boy as an abominable intruder. It came to pass finally that she could not tolerate Ishmael or his mother, fearing the day they might conspire to do Isaac harm. Thus, she came with her complaint to Abraham, "Drive away that slave-girl and her son," Sarah insisted. "This slave-girl's son is not to share the inheritance with my son Isaac."

Abraham was sorely distressed. One does not repay God's generosity with injustice. Yet he had no doubt that the child of God's promise, Sarah's son, was the choice of his heart, however clear the laws of patrimony. He had to concede wisdom to Sarah in anticipating the conflict that must arise; but... at this point, God himself spoke up for Sarah, "Do not distress yourself on account of the boy and your slave-girl. Grant Sarah all she asks of you, for it is through Isaac that your name will be carried on."

Abraham bowed his head. "This decision is hard on me, my Lord. I accept Thy will which is mysterious to me. Later generations will be Thy witness." Early the next morning, Abraham took some bread and a skin of water and with this, he sent Ishmael away with Hagar. Abraham was at peace, watching them depart, for he knew that God was with the boy. Had He not said, "But the slave-girl's son I will also make into a nation, for he is your child too."

"What has God held back from Abram?" Satan cried out in protest. Satan never used Abraham, the name of the second baptism. "Look how He bribes him! Even the serpent, He has forbidden to wink!"

God did not reply to Satan; calling out instead, "Abraham! Abraham!" in a loud voice.

"What about Ishmael?" Satan flung forth his challenge; not really concerned about justice, but more as a goad, "Should the elder son water his weeds, while the younger claps the harvest with both hands to his bosom?"

Meanwhile, Abraham had given heed to the summons of God, and he went forth from his fields that he might be alone in the sight of the Lord. Thus, he bowed thrice and remained with his head touching the soil.

"Here I am, my Lord."

"More land, my Lord?" Satan interjected quickly; laying bare his cynical anticipation. "More stars in the heavens? More sand by the sea?"

"Take your son, your only child, Isaac, whom you love, and go to the land of Moriah. There you shall offer him as a burnt offering on a mountain I will point out to you."

The stunned silence was Satan's not Abraham's. He who had bargained with such heroism for the lives of the evil-doers within Sodom and Gomorrah, risking the wrath of God … said not one word to save the life of his own son.

On the third and last of the silent days before the peak, Abraham bade his servants to remain behind with the donkey; making the gesture with his hands, for he could not separate his tight-pressed lips. But speak he must; and the sound came out like a sigh escaping from the cracks between his dry lips. "The boy and I will go over there; we will worship and come back to you."

It was Isaac who carried the wood for the fire. The knife was under the white knuckles of his father's fist. For the first time in their journeying, Isaac dared to intrude on his father's broodings. "Father," he began timidly, slow of speech; then he paused, seeing the bulge of veins on his father's forehead; that suddenly, his age was on him with white hair and loose folds of flesh.

"Yes, my son."

"Father, I see the fire; and, here is the wood; but, *where is the lamb, where is the lamb for the burnt offering?"*

What dialogue would Satan have provided here? "I am the lamb! God is my wolf!"

Adam: "Why was I given sight for this vision?"

Enoch: "Take me instead!"

Noah: "The rainbow, God, the rainbow!"

"My son, God himself will provide the lamb for the burnt offering." Heavy of heart, Abraham fumbled with the knife and dropped it to the ground.

Isaac, alarmed by Abraham's pallor, rushed to retrieve the weapon, pressing it into his father's hands, and Abraham was halted by the look in his eyes, all of his innocent, youthful love spilling out: "My father, you are ill, you must rest!" He was pulling Abraham down to the altar, indeed, sitting next to him....

Such a thing must be done swiftly, no time to stroke the soft, curly hair once more, no time to gaze with delight at the play of dimples in the soft round flesh of his cheek ... with a hoarse cry, Abraham pushed Isaac full-length on the altar, holding him there with one arm, the other raised high, the knife reflected in Isaac's eyes, his bewilderment turning to fear: "What have I done, father? Nooooo, father, noooo!" Abraham closed his eyes, not to witness it...

Thus, God witnessed Abraham's faith; and it warmed his heart. And an angel took the words from His lips, stopping the arm of Abraham, and the life of Isaac was spared. Abraham wept until there were no more tears in him, clutching Isaac to him fiercely, running his hands over the boy's face over and over again, praising God for what he had been spared.

The Great Ram, the one who had been there in waiting since the birth of the world, now came forward; its large and splendid horns were caught in the brambles of that same bush whose burning vessel would one day hold the voice of God. And the Great Ram did not resist while Abraham prepared the alternate sacrifice for his son. Only the horns were spared the flame; the large and splendid horns were reserved for the Day of the Messiah; when they will sound forth three stupendous blasts summoning the quick and awakening the dead to their judgement.

Part 6
THE THIRD TEMPTATION

Make of Satan what you will; but don't neglect his supreme audacity. No earthly thespian has dared as many roles, no musician has worked with as large a chorus and when it comes to over-painting the canvas, which masterpiece was already complete—only Satan would dare! Who else, with all that command of prose, a baker of words, kneading and twisting a phrase for any occasion, who else, desperate for an apt image, a curdling retaliation; who else, with random whim, would be pretending to strum an imaginary guitar, indulging in one of those ditties whose light freight was never meant for a penetrating voyage?

"Should One expect veneration from another generation?

Simple! Make them master, set them free; give them all their eyes can see.

Bribery?

Give them sons, give them gold;

'Faith' can be bought and sold."

Satan's response to the existence of Abram was a study in adaptability. He set up the twins of doubt and despair; bid them waltz and engage in light and brilliant repartee, then changed the tune; fate and doom, tapped one and the other dancer on the shoulder, in a dizzying change of pace. The touch was light. Each dancer wore a cynical, smiling mask; beguiling was the black swirl of their robes. Yet, all was not as playful as it seemed; in fact, grim and desperate; Satan's way of closing the curtain over his concern. There was a new force on earth; new in its awesome potential; its availability to every man.

Jesus was not lulled by Satan's light touch and good humor. He saw him as a black butterfly, flitting back and forth, moving its wings casually pretending a careless interest, having nothing to do with the heart of the flower, yet deathly concerned. He saw that the black wings were, indeed, mechanical, that, at the point of the looping antennas were globules of poison that had been borrowed from the serpent for the moment before another Eden.

As it watched him, Jesus pinched the tips of its black wings and flung it away; but it came back, it came back on the tip of the black feather on Satan's cap, just as Satan appeared. This once, he managed not to seem obscene; dressed in soft and dark silks; noble and ancient; resting on a jeweled sword; chin slightly elevated; posing it would seem, for Jesus to regard him in his dignity.

Jesus knew that the sands in the desert were running out, that it would be the end of the forty days in less than three score hours. He could understand the frustration of Satan even that he stood erect, that so far, it had been a stalemate. That the Prince of Darkness was now in full regalia served as a warning to Jesus and he watched cautiously; thanking God with humility that he had arrived this far.

His voice quivered as he told Satan, "I see the child with the new voice in the world, and he will be Abraham."

"Oh," replied Satan, rubbing his eyes, and yawning. "Abram again. What's the score? If you were God and I were Adam, seeing what was to become of it, surely we'd throw the pieces back in the box. Speaking for Adam, wherever he is, I would not have bothered beginning. Would you, Jesus? What can you do without power?"

At the word power, Jesus saw that Satan's left eye involuntarily began to sparkle, changing colors in kaleidoscopic succession and reflecting transparent images in flight; one of which would seem to be Eve, holding the forbidden fruit up to her lips.

"Unclean!" Jesus shaped the word slowly and forcibly, not concealing his distaste. He would have turned away, but wherever he turned Satan was there, either leaping in the air, or crouched down like a dog. *Power!* The word rose of itself again on stilts now, sounding hypnotically in Jesus' ear, ringing like a bell, become sibilant. And then, that hissing he heard was the wind. Black stars in a white sky! Jesus saw that his body had left the earth behind, that Satan's hand was touching his shoulder, that they were both falling forward at great speed in what seemed to be one of many tunnels in the sky.

"In Thy hands!" Jesus managed to cry, though each word was a torture in his lungs.

A circling speck below became more than a point above the clouds. It turned out to be a fingertip of the earth: the highest peak of a mountain range. The darkness whirled and fell back, funneled into a yet higher trough. Now, Jesus found himself alone, beside Satan who was turning to him with gusto and obvious pleasure, saying, "Now you have God's view of things. A little different, eh?"

Suddenly, he turned melancholy, sitting down on the jut of a large boulder, bent over, chin in hand, brooding. "It doesn't play anymore," he commented wearily; looking old and tragic then searching the round horizon for the dawn, expecting it sooner. There was an eerie light under Satan's skin, a radium ghost of another time and place and person; iridescent fires highlighting the sweep and tumble of successive low-key emotions. Out of all this came that voice; rumbling in its depths like lava ready to heave through all openings. *"How do you know that I am not really the true God?"*

This was the reality to which Jesus had come, not knowing where he was, or what was about to happen and hearing this. Why had God not interfered?

Satan swallowed a sob; and for once it was certain that these emotions were genuine, "That I was not vanquished by the Evil One who now sits enthroned on the neck of joy and pleasure, calling good 'evil' and evil 'good?'"

This was no random flight of an arrow seeking a target. Satan groaned, "I feel the beginnings of each new day. Infirmities," he pointed to his bowels, "but not of the flesh. A wrenching plague of a pain that shouldn't be, but is. And herbs and spells will not prevail against it! I think of God in exile, how He would feel. He would feel this same sharp memory of the first dawn, the one before there was an earth, of such indescribable beauty that only the One who has known the fullness of peace within the fullness of revelry can countenance its pale and subdued reflection. I can forget that I heard the angels, though their voices come back to me at times, but this," again he pointed to the lower portion of his abdomen, "it hits me here; and I realize that the greatest punishment of all … is not to forget!"

"If I forget Thee, oh Lord," Jesus began in contrast; but Satan cut in, "… let my right arm wither. No, no, no, no; it's not the same.

You can't understand."

He shook his head forlornly as the first rays of the sun were beginning to enter the sky. "There!" Satan pointed to the light-entered darkness. "It begins!"

His voice fell short; then, making an effort to confront his gloom, he blurted out sharply, "Now the pain is gone." He looked even more downcast.

The soft and golden light came into the sky like a stalking cat and the darkness retreated by slow degrees. Dark-winged clouds took flight like frightened birds. Now, only the haze was left intact; yet, beginning to flutter as the light penetrated, racing outward from dark wounds tinged with amber and magenta auras. A gasp! A sudden laugh! And the light sprawled out in full possession, multi-tongued, licking all the edges of the horizon whose evidence was yet that there had been night. The upturned cup of milk curved equally to all points of the compass; and against the white-chalk surfaces, the spires of great cities within great kingdoms rose, gleaming magically, returning the sun's rays to its newly-risen source. The sun had entered like a fallen skein of wool.

"All mine!" Satan broke the spell; his voice trembling with passion. "All mine!" and his eyes grew sharp like rodent's, scampering back and forth restlessly. "My prize! My kingdom!"

Jesus had been caught up in the joy of the morning; that God had granted him a new day of life within His sight. It was Satan who had ridden the moon into the sea. It was Satan whose voice grated with sick humors; who brought fright to blasphemy; a burden to the morning.

Satan was driving against time. Dispense with any preliminaries and let the fierce energies rage past any and all subtleties; fire the forest, setting to flame the underbrush. "A city full of Adams and Eves . . . scurrying for the first bite of the fruit!" he stated his theme brusquely, then opened the hive. "Forget compassion! It's never given nor would it be understood, except as surrender. You worry over your flock, and the sheep smother you inside their fur. Without sharp teeth and the whip, they'd walk all over you and know, know they're stepping on your face."

He faced Jesus, as if speaking to a comrade-in-arms, nudging him, "Should we be more proud than the Angel of Death, who, in the end, gets it all? Is it wrong to relieve the burden of that breath? Haven't I mixed the breed enough to fix the seed?"

Satan held out his hands to show his innocence; then looked up quickly, trying not to be crude, "*If I did nothing at all, Man would fall!*"

Satan waited, and Jesus replied, as always, in those few words whose impact is its Source, "I believe that what comes from God, as it was, can be returned to Him. I believe in confession, mercy and redemption. It is my faith in the soul of man that it can ask for and receive a higher baptism and be numbered among the blessed."

In his state at this moment, this was not what Satan wanted to hear. The same intransigence! "Bishop Abram again!" he shouted, and his face grew dark with rage. For the first time, Satan's sense of impotence had boiled over to that point where previously pride had impeded; when physical violence is all that remains. The tips of Satan's claws touched Jesus' flesh, before retracting. In conceding his own fallibility, Satan was compelled to recognize that the rising new power on earth had potential beyond any human adversary; that the uncomfortable reality he had hoped to avoid was close on his heels, that he must divide and share his kingdom.

"I give you the cities!" the words tumbled from Satan's lips, hearing themselves and wanting to return as if they had not been formed and released. What followed, however, was completely involuntary. "I give to you and thine the kingdoms of the world and all their splendor ... and all the souls within!" he added that afterthought "Even the babes unborn; the blessed and the uncircumcised!" He clutched at Jesus' shoulder. "Take all the rogues and scoundrels as well! That's why you came into the world, isn't it?"

His hands tightened on Jesus' shoulder, opening and closing; resisting the circle of his throat; then, bursting loose with a cry of agony in which contempt blended with torment, "You've won your forty days. Open up the gates of Sheol. Release me with the rest!" Satan thrust his chin forward, retaining a last vestige of pride. His chest heaved, he was panting and making explosive sounds with his lips. Even then, a shrewd look came back into his eyes; too late to be hidden. He closed his lids, hiding undersea what should not be seen.

"Really, Jesus, what are we dealing with here? How does one meet a bribe except with a better one! Seize the moment, my keys or His lock! What have you to do with these bottomless desires, never to be fulfilled, extinguishing themselves, contaminated by their own touch, diluting their source, fugitive, criminal, ashamed to raise their heads; stooping to guile and deception; murderous toward the exceptional one who dares! That you came on earth with a mission is already an open secret. But what you don't seem to grasp: that it is not you who lead, but that you are being led. God needs help! Why else all the messengers, patriarchs, prophets, Messiahs, and what not! All right, if it is within you to proclaim the millenium, do it already! Proclaim it! I give you the world, make better use of it!

"In whose name?" Jesus asked with calculated naivete.

"That thou may be like God!" Satan was virtually screaming. His face kept taking on and putting off emotions, in a charade of the entire armory of sin.

"I ask of thee. Can it stand straight and firm before the altar of God?"

Satan looked nonplused, not wanting to understand. "The power is thine!"

"Canst thou be reborn? What power can you have that you can exchange it! Canst thou be reborn?"

"I am *forever!*" Satan roared, then he caught himself. His face grew long and solemn. "Only this I need: thy tribute! That you fall on your knees and worship me. I mean, what you do each morning and evening for the Other so many times that I'd begun to think there were no feet under your knees."

This was the game of God and Adam, Eve and the serpent, wind-up toys repeating themselves over and over again. Now, as Jesus spoke; each word was a hammer stroke: the game ended; the springs, unwound, *"You must worship the Lord your God, and serve Him alone."*

Part 7

FAITH—THAT FLAW!

"Before God formed the image of Adam and planted him in His garden, I was. I am! I will be! Child of which creation, would you call me, Jesus? Can you think with the mind of God? Why, then, should you venture to predict Satan?"

"I do not know all the aces you have shown me, Satan, except the one which is your own. When you take exception, I recognize you! You have shown to my gaze those undercurrents that weaken the base rock, splitting its fastness and inviting the sea to invade the shore. I see you, and there's the flaw! Every grain of sand is accounted for!"

Satan laughed shortly, then wrinkled the corners of his lips. He was not amused. Time was thinning out. The contest would never again be so direct; or in such close quarters, without intermediaries. He leaped forward on both feet, shrieking, "You are blind! Perfectly orthodox—but blind! You're walking the road to Eden, aren't you? You dream of the fruit, and the head upon you is full of eternal life, blessed! blessed! Take the hand close to your own, no eye is needed where there is no darkness. Who can see through joyful tears? Tears that become crystals of salt when you arrive in Sheol still holding my hand!"

Satan paused, observing that some truth or other had reached Jesus and was pulling at his roots. Such a curious armory of *virtues*, he mused to himself, keeping a sharp eye on the alert for consequences, that humility must give him pause in the midst of battle, thereby losing the overreach and slackening momentum.

"There are those who would exceed God in virtue," Jesus began sadly; but Satan would not let him continue: "Exceed God? Exceed man!" Satan shouted, staring at Jesus pointedly. "Are you trying to shorten the difference between man and his next condition? Foolish saint! How far apart is sanctity from sin? Would you take heaven by storm? Go! Go beyond the first limits, Jesus! See where you arrive! In this less immediate time, there is no difference between the flaw and perfection. The flaw is perfection! Haven't you understood that yet? Look back at that dung heap which is the world you know, since you haven't really left it yet. Even you, with your fine-tuned senses, after just a lick at paradise, want more and more. Virtue has no end ... or do you grow less virtuous as you gain more? Insatiability: would you not call it that? Fidgety with fuss, fuming, frantic, frenzied; a fanatic will bent on the *whole*, the *total;* less and less subtle, clutching at nothing with opening and closing fists; caught up in the maze of phantasmagorias. Thus your holiness, Jesus. Have you any idea Jesus, should the miracle raise you far up high where I have been, how fast one descends?! The secret law of the universe is *this*, not perfection itself! But the authority to *define* perfection. The last and final justice is power, the barbed fist of the Holy Ghost.

"Poor, poor Jesus! With the soul of a fly, trying to scale glass walls into heaven! First, they remove your wings, Jesus! It's not your game, Jesus; but have you ever taken the wings off a fly? Most little humans have. It would profit the point, however, if you were to watch the unwinged one surrounded by walls of glass, rising, falling, rising, falling, I could sing it with a lilt: rising, falling, until overcome by weariness, the rhythm begins to change: ri...sing, fall...ing. Strike the glass with a flick of your nail, and behold! New energies. It becomes inventive, experimental, walking up sideways, then backwards, straining in all its parts. Its antennae wiggle-waggle; trying to make suction against the glass; to do what it was never intended to do; give leverage for the upward thrust. And when that fails and no amount of scratching and pounding can penetrate the glass, it lies on its back making slow circles with its feet that finally cease. Dead, you think. Just touch it with the tip of your finger; and it leaps several times higher than before, almost exceeding itself with fear and frustration. *You've leaped outside the glass at the prod of His finger, Jesus.* Else, why would He want to show you off to me, here in the wilderness?"

"You watched a cocoon Satan! Not a fly! A cocoon whose name was Abram. And when you thought to torture him with your finger, it was the shell you touched; the empty skin from which Abraham had flown; and you were blinded by the color of his wings. And it came to pass in the nine and ninetieth year of the first-born of Terah; that God turned His eye fully on the son of the idol-maker; and made His pleasure known. In the fullness of His spirit, He said to the son of His breath: You shall no longer be called Abram. You shall be Ab Hamon, father of a multitude, Abraham. I will make you into nations, and your issue will be kings. The whole land of Canaan will be yours. And I will be your God. And when the Lord had spoken, he made known that seal in the flesh, which would stand beside the rainbow. "

Satan burst into a profanity of laughter. "That curious covenant of the foreskin! To be man by becoming less than man." Satan smiled, then showed his true humor, raging: "If I had not any faith with Whom would I be contending?"

Part 8
TOWARD MORNING

The first flame had come into the night, burning unseen under the still invisible horizon.

"You shall learn the kindness of mere living presence," Satan had said before departing. At the time, it had seemed to Jesus not much more than a commentary on Satan's own plight. Yet here it was again; returning this time more introspectively. The memory had air in it, after sinking like flotsam, to rise this way from under a motionless sea, wet grass in its hair.

Jesus looked at it again; letting its filaments reflect another facet of light. As his imagination caught firmer hold of Satan's thought; he began to recognize how much more there was in it. *This is what Adam, expelled from Eden had seen.* Wait! Wait! It was only one of the crystalline depths! *It was also the experience of Lucifer,* the brightest of all the stars, falling, falling, burning as it fell, losing its light, gathering speed. But caution! On guard against the inexhaustible subtleties of Satan: one tip of that sword, the least lodgment, and it festers perniciously.

What was it that bound the anguish of the fallen man to the charred and blackened angel who was now Satan? *Mere living presence.*

There was the clue, the key word, that which brings the darkness into the light. The *kindness* that comes to mere is the last compromise; the final and most terrible of choices... Anything, anything but total death!

What defeat is this that would accept despair against total oblivion? Jesus shuddered; knowing the reply that Satan would make: *the hope for vengeance! Anything but total death!*

Seen in microcosm, the drama repeats itself among all the generations from Adam, opening their eyes with shock and surprise that they are not in Eden; then clawing at the sky with sharp fingers and vainglorious ambitions.

Jesus had touched the icy side of the glacier which had been the impediment once before, and as he gazed up where Adam and Eve had made their futile ascent, he saw how much higher there was yet to climb. The moment he hesitated, Satan's words came back to mind: forty days and nights were not enough. If Jesus had had any illusions about his ministry, this quick, stabbing insight would have been fatal but as Jesus saw it, sustenance was an endless string of faith, like lanterns in the storm, keeping a flame alive in hurricane winds. Find the part of man first touched by the breath of God!

The black lilies were blooming in the night air, giving off their heavy musk. The spores were in flight; tiny spines of feathers floating, giving off a sweet and sickening odor. The heaviness added to the fatigue Jesus felt, half-closing his eyes, and he had to struggle against the temptation to give up all restraint, and sleep.

It was in small and silent ways, Jesus realized, that Satan's attacks are more successful. No armies in full regalia! Just a sly hint, a touch, a taste, a whisper, call it sleep, not suicide; not death, just returning life to the seed.

"WHAT DIFFERENCE!" There was that hollow-echoed voice in the night, sighing with loneliness. *"It all ends!"*

Jesus was fully awake now; lighting a candle for one lantern. "Only evil ends," he shouted back. The silence was mournful at first, rehearsing itself. Then, the reply came back: "Then life is evil; since it ends!"

The refrain was taken up by a chorus of wee voices: "It ends! It ends!"

The whole weight of the forty days was in this next moment. It was in the struggle for this meaning that Jesus had sowed his seed in the desert; for he had seen the tragedy of human time; that reason had no hold on it. The answer must go beyond faith, a miracle! A joining with the mind of God.

Jesus broke through; the seed sent forth green beyond any doubt, coming to blossom in his full conviction: *"Only death ends!"*

The challenge to despair was, in fact, the first step out of the desert for Jesus. The immortal soul was more than the sum of its parts, and this was the truth of Creation and the power of God.

"Only death ends!" Faith had its answer. Order had come out of chaos, and the dilemma of either/or was false in the face of the One and Only.

The last night had reached its first station.

Part 9
PROLOGUE TO DAWN

The fierce and searching winds were now in the desert, moving briskly behind clouds of sand. "Now!" Jesus told himself, feeling the cold; trying to penetrate the mists for the face of Satan.

It had arrived at the time just before sunrise when the long night is at its lowest ebb, seemingly, without end; drained of hope, enervated. This is the time, time without sleep, when the sick make their last agonized stand; raising their heads to the murkiness, then returning their souls to the encroached darkness. This is the time for the faithless to extinguish their own lights. *This is Satan's hour;* when the catch of his net is at its fullest.

"Jesus ben Joseph!" There he was! Jesus heard himself paged from fast-moving black clouds; from hollow distances under the surface sand; then, from behind his back, as Satan appeared, smiling broadly like an old friend expecting to be welcomed.

Jesus turned swiftly. At least, now the night had definition. "Where have you been?"

Meanwhile, Satan's eyes had been moving in loose sockets, pulsing, bubbling, probing what was not there to find. The amalgam of disbelief and incredulity merely cushioned the shock of stubborn evidence, Jesus had gone through the night inside himself, not only surviving, but, indeed, grown stronger!

Satan saw the phosphorescent glow of that skeleton before him— call it Jesus! Call the bones the knit of a man! And Satan staggered back, for once without immediate recourse, naked. There no longer existed any real distinction between the body and soul of Jesus!

How was it possible for a mere issue from the womb? Adam, perhaps, fresh into Eden but, knowing the taste of the fruit. Enoch, without sin, but having lived among men in their world.

Flash upon flash of insight, rapidly exploring this phenomenon among men, exalting and transcending the pristine clay touched by the holy breath of God. What should have been a celebration of bells was for Satan a slow, funereal knell, burying Death. For, if it were possible once within man's nature; *it could happen again,* conceivably, the gate before Eden would fall; obliterating that other Fall!

All this had taken full tide in Satan's mind in just one instant; so that his reply to Jesus' question came almost immediately; and he replied as once before he had replied to God, "Round the earth, roaming about."

Jesus understood at once both what Satan had spoken and what he had not said aloud, and he responded to the question that had not been asked, with one word, "Abraham!" With this, he gave testimony to the first full dawn of God's providence; that God's search for what had been the first Adam was not in vain.

Without a word, Satan drew aside, letting Jesus see the fleshy face with the tortured eyes of Simeon Ben Ezra, sometimes called Temporus. Simeon was at that moment waiting in the atrium of a Roman palace just outside the walls of Jerusalem.

It was true, as Satan had said, that Simeon had taken his own depth when he had left Jesus out of sight; but now he had come with that unlikely and mysterious spin of the wheel back to the same number. A light flared up inside him that he had not believed existed. Simeon paused, took heed; he cannot ignore it; otherwise, he would become abhorrent to himself. His rationale must find a voice; reach out and be heard by Jesus. The betrayal was weighed in gold but even as he waited in the shaded garden, he saw those burning eyes reflected in the still pool, mirroring that disconcerting contact in the desert, and he had to cope with it, or not continue.

Satan gave him that opportunity.

"Everyone has their price! And if you're out there in the desert being tested, or testing yourself against Satan, it's a big one! It's no secret that Satan offers the key, lock and all, to the prophets, the Garden of Eden alone with Eve, for one; hearty and alive at everyone else's death bed, for another.

"Either that, or resist, and get Heaven. One way, you're a prince! Choose the other, you're a saint! The bribe on both sides — not bad, Jesus! Hear me out, Jesus; and you'll know why I fled from you. First off, let me say that never have I felt so much love for a man, not to my own father; never have I been so close to returning it!

"If, knowing myself, I had known I could take myself out of the world: well and good! But not me. I had a sweet tooth when I was born and it never left me!

"Perhaps it would have been better if I had been born a slave with a slave's appetites, and I was up for sale on the block, and you passed by, and bought my body, and put everything else that fits inside?

"Perhaps, if you yourself had already sinned before ... which I did not believe! If you had seen my lust reflected in your own; and, pitying your own fall, pitied me.... That's it! *You have not been truly tempted unless you succumbed to temptation before!*

"I don't mean the choice between underworld banquets with red tablecloths for saints who spurn the feast for white tablecloths in the upper spheres. Such a choice most of us never get, and if we dream about them we can't believe our dreams, so it's not a temptation.

"Our temptations, if you're going into the day-to-day world on feet instead of wings, are not staged in coliseums. Who's interested in small hungers and meals on a pittance? Where's the spectacle in the multitude of errant impulses buzzing, drumming, biting with tiny teeth on our daily lives? So, once in awhile a restless mind comes to fancy, as mine has. It's only a step above drowning. Don't you see it? What surrounds us? The petty coincidences; and all those unpredictable encounters with their predictable endings!

"What answer do you have to age and physical deformity? I have seen with my own eyes the sad faces of small children: my own! Shall I drown them in a well out of sight? I have seen my own greed and lust mirrored back at me from every face in the crowd. Every day my soul is taken off-guard; and in the choicelessness of 'natural' events, in the war against my dreams, I surrender to my own defenses, now, at least my dream has its own will.

"*Satan has no need to bargain with us....*" Simeon's voice jerked back into the night; nor did Jesus need wonder what was happening. He lifted his hand, knowing it was futile; hearing the refrain of Satan's previous commentary: 'This one comes as a warning of what the others are like.' Then, more direly, *'He will betray you.'*

Whether or not Satan had rehearsed and provided the dialogue was not as important to Jesus as the semblance to truth that can be built on the ashes of Sodom and Gomorrah. Look who speaks for man, with a vengeance!

There was Satan again, forcing the initiative after reading Jesus' thoughts: "Why man? Why not Satan? Not Satan! Lucifer!" It was a wild and strange summing-up of Satan's own forty days; opening for the first time that terrible pocket of hope, desperately trying to mask its urgency with such turbulent phrases, "You have not redeemed your purchase!" As if to say, why are you not my Messiah? When God brought us together, was it not for my redemption?

Unwittingly, Satan answered his challenge; making it clear what he truly felt; that the hope he had kept hidden so well was truly without desire. The fury burst from his lips, "You will not negate me!"

He pounded his fist into the palm of his hand, then struck at the air with dagger blows. Clearly, the impediment was Jesus. Overwhelmed by frustration, he let out a sudden shriek not unlike the cry of a trapped tiger, lunging out with its claws; coming closer to Jesus and raising his fist, "You! You! Are you more than Enoch, living out your life without sin? Your *whole* life, without sin!"

In the face of such last minute extremities, Jesus thought it the better part of wisdom to remain silent. Unnecessarily, because Satan was off on another tack; transforming a silence which he could no longer abide into a tirade that scattered seeds over a wide area, needing only one root for doubt, "Don't you think? If you could see the third and final act before the first begins: how boring, boring, boring all those poses and pretensions!

"Yet, each time I must wait and wait and wait, only to watch the same bone chewed in the same corner with the same possessiveness—as if the bone had marrow left in it!

"Dull, dull, *dull!* Ask me what it's all about, and I'll reduce it for you simply to one word: *contradiction.* The whole nut is within this shell! But I'll let you find that one out for yourself.

"Anyhow, if I asked the same question of you; you would reduce it all to love, love, *love,* wouldn't you? Like a wound-up toy watching a wound-up clock ... back and forth ... back and forth ... perfect harmony, perpetual joy; perfect harmony, perpetual joy, as if the breath of God in Adam could be made to function mechanically!

"Don't agree or disagree with me! Just keep your eye fixed on the second hand, back and forth ... back and forth. Go ahead, keep pace!

"Now, tell me. Aren't you ready for variety: speed up, slow down, syncopate ... no? Not yet? Give it a few more millennia: perfect harmony, perpetual joy. Bear in mind, as you must, that the Clock Maker is an inventor; a genius with an itch! Is there only one form of perfection?

"Aha! To create a minor version of Oneself that reproduces itself. Back and forth ... back and forth ... until, one day: the COMMAND!

"Should I offend you, Jesus? Would the universe stop spinning if I told you that He who made Adam, that same day *He planted that tree in Eden Himself! He put the knowledge of good and evil in it, and I had already taken my taste of it!*

"Guilty, if I *am* guilty, if there is such a thing as guilt, except for the powerless! If adjustment can be called sin, if there *is* such a thing as sin, then, it was I who made the adjustment. No more did I do than give reason a prod and reroute it through the senses.

"Is that so much of a contradiction beside: Let there be Light and there was light, and the light shone first and symbolically on that tree in Eden? Where's the fun, Jesus? What's the game?"

Jesus raised his eyes upward; itself a benediction. His voice was a song, "Thank you, Father, that I have been given eyes to see the ways of Satan. I might have been born blind and not seen the nightmare for what it is; I might have been lame and unable to turn away. For this alone, my heart rises from the dust to Thee; and I rejoice that my tongue has found a new voice to proclaim Thy everlasting glory. In sheltering both the dove and raven, You have revealed to us that night follows day, and day follows the night; telling us about life and death, that we may witness our faith redeemed... "

Satan caught the tone of the song Jesus sang, and he mocked him in the same voice, "Back and forth, back and forth ... and they call Satan a sorcerer! Who holds you captive? Did I hypnotize you? Raise your heart from the dust, when all the time the dust is in your eyes! Far better for you, while there is yet time, that you abscond from your vows, take God's hand, if you will, like Enoch; and be led on a leash to that great Unconscious where reality is not afraid of being overtaken. Here, I will show you! "

Satan held out his fist; did some things to it with his other hand. It seemed like madness; confirmed by what followed, "Here is Enoch! The puppet of Him!"

Indeed, when Satan removed his other hand, Jesus saw that the fist had taken on the form of a face, full with hair and a beard; eyes, nose, mouth. Either it spoke, or it was a masterpiece of ventriloquism, or Satan's fist could speak, defining itself, "I am the nightside of Enoch. I am the moon to his sun, what Enoch might have been if God had not walked away with the unfinished part of him. I sin, and I am sinned against."

Jesus stepped back, and said the prayer that puts to rest awakened golems, and the eyes of the thing went black.

Satan's lips curled up cruelly, and with a quick motion, he opened his fist, widening his fingers to show there had been nothing there. He laughed, seeing that Jesus was offended. "What do you expect: births without deaths?" Then, corrosively, "Think of all the visitors you *might* have had. You were spared the Sodomists and every one of Noah's neighbors, except for your cautious prayers."

For once, Jesus agreed. Satan made half a fist again, and looked down on it ruefully, "The trouble is, what remains with me is the refuse of your saints. This *could* have been Enoch...."

His voice became sad with an edge of irritation. "Shouldn't we assume that He leaves nothing unfinished? The unheard sound remains in the wind, the unfinished life finishes itself. Even if God Himself pulled down the very pillars of Creation what would arise from the rubble? His own breath, returning to its Source: sad, isn't it?" To prove his point, Satan's face broke out in a self-satisfied smile, pleased with himself, saying: "It's good to be Satan."

Jesus was abrupt with him. "Ask that of Lucifer!"

Satan quivered to the bristle; yet instead of an angry outburst, he began to waltz with an imaginary partner, tacking backwards to

Jesus, as if it were of no consequence. "You're right. No one, I suppose, would have chosen the grim bleakness of Sheol as it was. Since then, think of the company: Kings! Popes! Generals! Think of the conversations: the games of chess we play with living pieces and the earth roped off in perfect squares. Checkmate! Nobody beats me! I sacrifice my pawns with abandon!"

Satan paused in his waltzing, dismissing his imaginary partner with a bow before returning to his theme, "There is nary enough subtlety in your world to conceive of punishment becoming its own reward. Maybe, you do, in some perverted and inverse manner; starving the flesh to feed the spirit and all that; but, I'm speaking of imposed punishment, when the tight cage expands and the prison becomes the universe. In the theology of Sheol, we call that 'milking the udderless cow'"

Jesus cut in impatiently on that phrase, "The dust of Cain, the echo of Simeon's voice, the puppet that was not Enoch. Is that the milk of Satan's wealth, that he expands himself, swelling with pride?"

Satan's glance went furtively over Jesus' features, forced to recognize that Jesus was taking the initiative more and more often, already looking beyond the desert into the world of men. His sharp eye for character and his genius for assessing reality had recognized that the moat was not breached; not at all ... yet. "And the stakes go higher," he mumbled to himself.

To his adversary, for that much respect Jesus had earned, he confessed, "Yes, I am not Lucifer. Nor would I be again! Nothing is more repressible than Satan's pride. You spoke of puppets, and dust, and attributes: *I am my own destiny!* I have recreated myself. He never made me as I am. If that were true, He would belong to Sheol, responsible for evil. What I was is not what I am! Merely by existing, I challenge Creation as He saw it. You said it well! I am not Lucifer, the prince in the constellation of stars. I am only one, Satan the king!"

The smile froze on his face. "Why else are you here if not to go home?"

Satan's conclusion rang in Jesus' ear like an alarm; as if Satan had blown out with one breath all the lanterns of faith, replacing them with fires of chaos, fear, and confusion. In a hushed voice, needing breath; Jesus looked over the desecration, asking Satan, "Do you not know that God can destroy you as if you had never been at all?"

Satan grinned. In a sense, he had finally gotten to Jesus—faith and all…forcing him to acknowledge the sword. Was it also a retreat from love, love, love? He looked at Jesus curiously. "Have you ever seen God face to face?" he asked with a more than momentary interest. "Can you credit man, beast or angel in direct combat, fist to fist with Him! Could He be less than Himself and remain God? A crack in infinity!" Satan became sarcastic. "A second-best Ruler who rules nothing at all; needing advice and permission! Jesus, He wins! Always, He wins! *But…!*"

While Satan paused for effect, Jesus pondered the famous 'but' of Satan: his signature, in fact. Hardly ever was it followed by a direct assertion. After these many days, Jesus had learned to anticipate rounded corners and a jagged route, veering sharply between doubt and negation.

"…*But,* the Winner loses! An abstraction, you think? Let me place it in its proper perspective lest you think I use words for their effect only. Look there, where the smoke rises over the battlefield. God has won, and the soldiers of both sides are beaten to the bone; denuded to the spirit right down to the bare 'free-will', which they would will away back to God … if they could raise their heads high enough!

"Would God accept? Inhale His own breath back again? Then deal with soulless creatures programmed to say yes! Oh, ye gilded angels! Ye prophets! Ye sniveling saints! Think of God watching an Adam on rails in Eden; turning its head away every time it passed that tree; programmed to say: "NO, not that fruit!' Is that what you would make of man?

Fortunately, God has the ambition that suits His glory. He wants Adam's 'yes' returned to Him by Adam's choice; so that Adam is heard, not God's decree. Recognize that difference, Jesus. All the wars, the fires and floods and earthquakes are caused by it, and the heart of it is in scripture … is scripture!

"See all the commandments, revelations, messengers, burning bushes, strange prophets with other tongues. How many ways does

God ask man to say 'yes'! NO, *not that fruit!* Does the canvas begin
to paint itself yet, Jesus?

"Let's say that Faith has won the battle. Yes, let's try God's way,
we've tried every other! Good! The gates of Eden open. We're in Paradise. It starts all over again. *NO, not that fruit!* What kind of statement is that to make to a man with free will? Is the memory of God
in his breath? Then, he must taste that fruit. Out! Out of Eden!

"Very well. Let's wipe out the memory of Adam and start in Eden
all over again. No tree, no fruit, no prohibition, no temptation.
Where does 'free will' go if it is from God, if not back to God! Being
what they are, Adam and Eve could never stand still. Can you hear
the beginning sounds of rebellion? Or would you call it: *the refusal
of God to share?* Out! Out of Eden!

"*But* ... why should God expect as much or more from man outside the gates as within Eden? What obstinacy! Wipe out the sins of
man, wipe out man, but keep the seed: the sins start all over again.
I tell you: the dead rode the Ark along with Noah!

"How many have there been like you, Jesus? Can you count them
on one hand and have fingers left over? So, perhaps you approach
some degree of perfection. As for the rest, can you expect perfection
from the imperfect, Jesus? The flaw was already in Adam! The flaw
entered the clay, Jesus! *The flaw was the breath of God.*

"There, I've said it, and if you'll desist from shock and surprise
and listen to me, I'll make it clear without needing faith to bolster
it. Whatever else we don't know about God, this much we do know:
that no part of God is less than another. Otherwise, there would be
an impurity. That part of God which entered the clay remains separate from the clay, rejects the union, while assuming the throne of
the Will. It's as simple as that: God rebels against Himself!

"Ah, but you'll say, why shouldn't that part of God which is the vital
breath in man sustain itself like a ship in a storm and carry its cargo
with it toward perfection? I can testify to that, or better still, Lucifer
can. The part which separates from the whole gains new characteristics
in its new environment. As Simeon called Temporus was wont to say:
the drunken habit comes after the first taste. Thus, with sin....

"I'll grant you that disparagement of nature which is your small claim to fame, Jesus. There are heroics in your sanctity which astonish even me and I'll grant you a virtuous grave ... even more! I'll pay tribute that you may have resisted the taste of the fruit on that tree in Eden.

"It's your mission that rankles me. That proud show of humility that takes confidence where God, so many times, has admitted failure. Jesus! Will man obey man sooner than God? Will you prohibit sin? Or spread it out where it grows best, at secret banquets, by another name?

"How will you bring about this Golden Age, this millenium without even a few thunderbolts in your pocket? Have you found the seed that was not from Adam?

"God has already won the Sabbath, Jesus. Mostly sin rests that day, and the ordinary man, who is not Jesus, refreshes himself for that ordinary day in an ordinary world where he is bound by God, in the name of ordinary moralities to make unwilling obeisance to the knotted spirit concealed in the flesh. Then, after the tired horn has sounded, Satan gets his due.

"You are defeated by victory, Jesus. *NO, not that fruit* ... I've lost ... I've won. I wait for the proper moment on the battlefield, taking my place with the less-than-corpses. You speak to them of ideals, of faith. I let their eyes range among the realities of death, disease and pestilence. You are shuddering. I hear a long sigh, Jesus. Why does your heart grow cold?"

There was no mistaking the rejection in the reply Jesus made, and because it was brief and to the point, after the long tirade in which Satan had invested so much, only to have his own words flung back at him; Satan could scarcely contain himself, waiting and shaking and frothing at the lips, after Jesus said to him, "No. Not that fruit!"

"Go!" Satan spewed up his reply. "Pick up your carpenter tools, and go! Go, collect your souls! This is your dawn ... harmonize with it. *But this one only!* One dawn, you've earned. Remember, though: the night is not far behind. The night, and the next one, and the one after that. Remember that when you applaud this sunrise. Even, I'll applaud with you, because I didn't expect to. Just remember after the curtain rises, the play is mine ... *mine!*

"Go! Go where you are bound to go. The lord Satan is where you cannot hide. Go, speak with God as you know Him, throw your voice in echoes through the mountains, search out where the sun hides, and put light in your path, strain upward from the highest thrust of stone: you touch a finger! Whose? What voice do you hear when you think God is speaking only to you?

"Go! Spy out the insides of the tabernacle where you hide the holiness from the eyes of the curious. And you shall find strings on the arms and legs of your Images!

"Go! Where the rays of light bend, father your disciples, collect souls in Jerusalem! You've made your sacrifices. Now, you bow your head at His feet ... His feet? You look up slowly, closing your eyes, not wanting to recognize yet, what if it were He, and you were blinded by the light?

"The suspense, the long silence that keeps you waiting. He, to Whom you have devoted all your life. "Open!' you are told, and you do so ... you are betrayed! He has gone elsewhere in the universe and forgotten you. Meanwhile, I have inherited the earth! *I am your Eucharist!*"

Jesus looked at Satan with open scorn. What other reply is there beyond Armageddon? Yet, there was the trace of a question....

Satan saw it, and let out an iron-throated roar, "Why does God tolerate me? You want to know, why does God tolerate me?" He turned on his heels abruptly, feeling the dagger thrust of pain he always felt when the light began to take over the sky.

"Perhaps, I, too, am a part of Him?"

Jesus understood it differently. What seemed like a long silence would have appeared as no answer to those whose ears were not properly attuned. The reply entered Jesus' heart and he took from it what he needed to know about Satan for surely they were destined to meet again in this world. *Satan was the absence of God's love.*

The last star was still resisting the oncoming light...

"Father!" Jesus cried out in a voice wild with joy. He stood on his toes and raised his head where there were no shadows on his face. His hands were like doves fluttering upward, "Thy will be done ... be done ... be done ...

OVER FOR OTHER BOOKS

many new and exciting releases

(If you are interested in any or all of these exciting new titles send us your name and address and we can send you a notice of publication with the price.)

By Way of the Cross By Carol J. Ross

Autobiography. When you read *By Way of the Cross* you will open yourself to tears of empathy and of joy as you see this woman struggling with terribly physical and mental crosses, scooped up into breathtaking visions of the supernatural world. Paperback. Full color photos. 468 pages. $12.50

Lost in the World: Found in Christ By Father Christopher Scadron

The story of a priest ordained at the age of 63 — As a young Jewish man Padre Pio predicated he would become a Priest. After years of floundering and sin as a naval officer and an artist, this unsually gifted and interesting man became a priest at 63! A tale all Catholics will find moving and deeply inspiring, it is also a must gift for any man you know who might be called to the priest hood at an age older than the usual. $12.50

Dancing with God through the Evening of Life
By Mary Anne McCrickard Benas

Unique insight into the world of the hospice worker and the patient relationship. The beautiful faithful outlook of a elderly man dying and the gifts he gives us through this experience. $12.50

The Third Millennium Women By Patricia Hershwitzky

Consider the sinking feeling many Catholics get when they see literature about preparing for this great event. They expect what they read or pretend to read to be true, but dull as dishwater. By contrast — here is a book that is wildly funny and also profound. Written by a "revert" (born Catholic who left and then returned), it is also ideal as a gift for those many women we know are teetering on the verge of returning Home.

Messages to the World from the Mother of God

Daily meditative pocketsize prayer book on the monthly messages given the visionaries in Medjugorji for the conversion of the World, back to her son Jesus. These messages for the World started in 1984 till the present. In 1987 the messages began on the 25th of the month (union of two hearts with the 5 wounds of Jesus) thus the 25th. These are from St. James Church in Medjugorji. Great Gift!!! $10.00

Children of the Breath By Martin Chervin

Who would have dared to challenge Creation if, at the close of each new day, God said, "It is perfect." Instead, His lips spoke "It is good..." and the serpent was already in Eden. Thus begins *Children of the Breath*, a startling journey into the desert where Christ was tempted for forty days of darkness and light. With immense clarity, lyricism, and humor, author Martin Chervin has delivered a powerhouse that will engage readers of any faith. $14.50

Radiating Christ By Fr. Raoul Plus, S.J.

To be a "Christ" is the whole meaning of Christianity. To radiate Christ is the whole meaning of the Christian apostolate. But to be a Christ for one's own personal benefit is not enough; we have to Christianize those around us; in a word we have to radiate Christ. $11.00

To order additional copies of this book:

Please complete the form below and send for each copy

CMJ Associates, Inc.
P.O. Box 661 • Oak Lawn, IL 60454
call 708-636-2995 or fax 708-636-2855
email jwby@aol.com
www.cmjbooks.com

Name _____

Address _____

City _____ State_____ Zip _____

Phone (   ) _____

	QUANTITY	SUBTOTAL

Children of the Breath
$14.50 each x _____ = $_____

Becoming the Handmaid of the Lord
$13.75 each x _____ = $_____

Ties that Bind
$ 8.50 each x _____ = $_____

The Cheese Stands Alone
$12.50 each x _____ = $_____

The History of Eucharistic Adoration
$ 4.00 each x _____ = $_____

The Bishop Sheen We Knew
$ 4.00 each x _____ = $_____

Behold the Man!
$12.25 each x _____ = $_____

+ tax (for Illinois residents only) = $_____

+ 15% for S & H = $_____

TOTAL = $_____

☐ Check # _____ ☐ Visa ☐ MasterCard Exp. Date ___/___/___

Card # _____

Signature _____

many new and exciting releases

Behold the Man, Simon of Cyrene By Father Martin DePorres
Inspired writing by a gifted new Author. This story shows us the
gifts given to Simon. Throught carrying the Cross with Jesus,
Simon shares with us the gifts we can expect by carrying our
daily crosses. $12.25

Becoming the Handmaid of the Lord By Dr. Ronda Chervin
The journals of this well known Catholic writer span her family
life as wife and mother, mystical graces sustaining her through
a mid-life crisis, the suicide of her beloved son, her widowhood
and finally a Religious Sister at the age of 58. Insightful,
inspiring & challenging. 327 pages of the heart. $13.75

Ties that Bind By Ronda Chervin
The story of a Marriage. This beautiful novel presents the wife's point
of view and the husbands point of view on the same conflict. The
author Dr. Chervin has written many books on Catholic life. *Ties that
Bind* is both funny and inspiring.
A great gift for couple thinking about marriage as well. $ 8.50

The Cheese Stands Alone By David Craig
(The formost religious poet of the day) A dynamite account of a radical conversion from the world of drugs to the search for holiness in the Catholic Church.
Realism & poetic imagery combine to make this a must for those who want the
real thing. Its a rare book that both monastic and charismatic — anyone
acquainted with the latter will love the chapter on misguided zeal,
aptly titled "Busbey Burkeley." $12.50

The History of Eucharistic Adoration By Father John Hardon, S.J.
In an age of widespread confusion and disbelief, this document offers unprece-
dented clarity in the most important element of our faith. I recommend that it
be prayerfully studied and widely circulated. It is thoroughly researched and
well documented, and promises to enlighten, instruct and inspire countless
souls to an undying love of our Eucharistic Lord. $ 4.00

The Bishop Sheen We Knew By Father Albert Shamon
A booklet filled with little known information from his Vicar, Fr.
Albert J.M. Shamon, Bishop Dennis Hickey and Fr. Mike Hogan,
the three remaining priests who worked under Bishop Sheen. A
chance to see the day to day workings of the acknowledged prophet
of our times. $ 4.00

Born, Unborn By Martin Chervin
What if inside this hospital bag, smashed in pieces, crushed to bits, evidence to
make one believe God didn't exist. What if, a second time on earth, the Spirit
of Mercy was giving birth, end of the voyage down to earth. In this bag, the
child Christ, returning to us... A second time, crucified.
                                                                 $ 9.95